THE MOLTEN KEY

T.L. WILSON

Map Design © T.L. Wilson

Cover Design © BY THE BROOKE DESIGNS

Edited by Emily A. Lawrence at Lawrence Editing

Identifiers:

ISBN: (ebook) 978-1-7782415-2-9

ISBN: (paperback) 978-1-7782415-0-5

ISBN: (hardback) 978-1-7782415-1-2

Content Warnings:

Violence, Language, death.

❀ Created with Vellum

For all the quirky kids who thought being different was a bad thing.

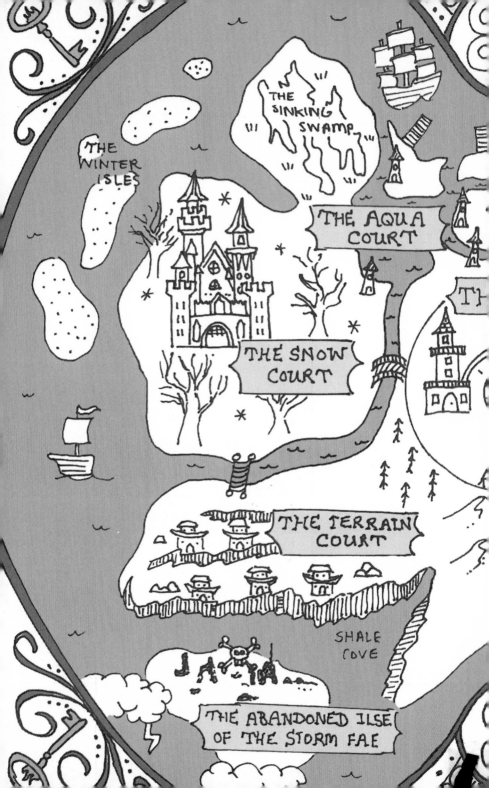

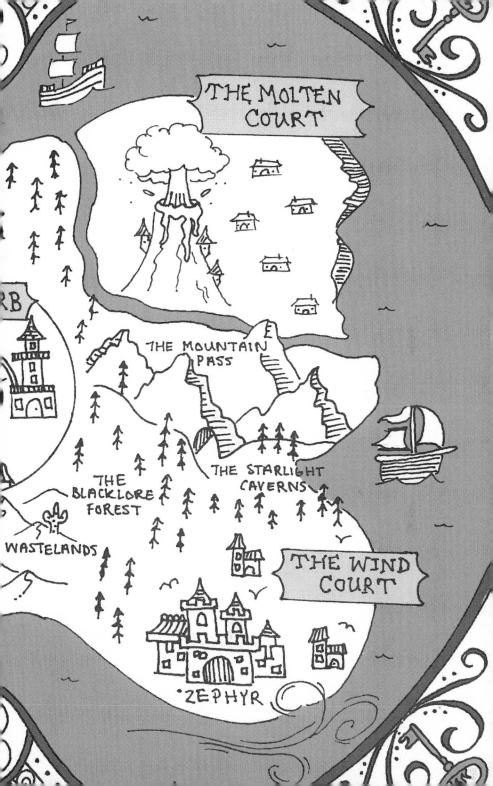

PROLOGUE

Smoke and ash billowed into the air, reminiscent of a puffball mushroom expelling its cloudy spores across the forest floor. Crackling clouds surrounded it, filled with neon purple lightning that forked across the sky. From his small cobblestone patio islands away, Teilio watched. He knew if he were any closer, he would be able to see the hail-like downpour of rock. He could almost feel the heat on his skin, causing a flush to creep up his neck towards his cheeks.

The eruptions were growing more frequent. The evacuations of nearby islands and the tragic fate of the people who chose to stay saturated the six o'clock news. Teilio had been following this increase in seismic activity occurring off the coast of Bark Beach for some time.

This was bad.

He knew what was happening.

He knew it would break soon.

He had always known one day it would break. His selfish choices had seen to that.

1

He had to do something about it before it was too late.
He was the only one who could.

CHAPTER 1

ONE WEEK LATER

A warm breeze shifted the branches of the flowering trees and kissed her face. Adelia Larson inhaled deeply, the fresh spring air washing through her lungs. It felt cleansing after a cold, dull winter. The gentle smell of the wet dew, the quickening of life in the forest, it was her favourite time of year. Not only was Bark Beach starting to show the first signs of spring—it was migration season.

Adelia crept through the labyrinth of underbrush, attempting to place each step with a precision and grace she most definitely didn't have. If only she could float above the forest floor. As it was, Adelia was doing a solid job of avoiding excessive noise. Not a single stick or leaf rustled. Her balance had improved remarkably over the last few years. Her physiotherapist had always told her she'd get better, but after the surgery, it had been hard to imagine she'd ever walk again, let alone hike.

She paused and listened, straining her ears as she focused in on an insect-like call through the songs of surrounding birds.

Just to the left, she decided.

Adelia readjusted her course and made her way towards a clearing. Rays of sun pierced through the canopy like arrows and warmed the ground under her. She felt the familiar weight of her binoculars strung across her shoulder swing as she stepped over a lichen-covered log. Emerging into a clearing, Adelia was momentarily distracted by the warm sun on her skin. Closing her eyes, she listened to the choreographed chaos of spring. It was an orchestra of birds' songs and calls, the trickle of a nearby stream, and the rustling of leaves in the wind. *This* was happiness. Standing here, *alive*, was a gift.

She stepped forward, and her curly, strawberry-blond hair caught on a branch, its spindly fingers yanking her backwards. She yelped in pain, causing the birds to scatter around the clearing as though a hawk had swept through. An abrupt, heavy silence settled over the forest.

"Typical," she muttered, exasperation edging her voice. So much for being quiet. Having a prosthetic leg didn't lend itself to being very stealthy in the first place.

"Adelia? Where did you go?" a gravelly voice called out.

Oh, shit. Right.

She was at work. She wasn't supposed to be going off course to search for birds.

Adelia scurried through the brush to where Ron was standing, hands on his hips.

"You can't leave me to scour the nets myself, Adelia. There are too many birds to collect." He held up an array of mismatched cloth bags, some already filled with squirming birds.

"Sorry. I won't get distracted again." She looked longingly over her shoulder at where she knew the Cerulean Warbler had been. She wanted nothing more than to continue her search for the bird. It was a lifer. Which meant in her twenty-two years of life—and almost that long birdwatching—she had *never* seen one. And hearing it sing didn't count.

Adelia worked at the Bark Beach Banding Centre, which was a small woodland area and birdwatching hotspot. There was a network of trails that wove through the area and she was currently assigned to do the first round of checks on the cobweb thin nets. They extended along both sides of the dirt path, and the morning dew that had settled on them made them shimmer in the sunlight as they shifted in the breeze.

Migrating birds couldn't see the nets as people could—they would fly into them, unaware of danger, and get stuck there until a worker could come and untangle them. Then the birds were put into small cloth bags and brought back to the banding centre where someone would record each bird. It would be banded with a shiny metal bracelet to help researchers keep track of its species numbers.

Gravel crunched beneath her feet as she grabbed some cloth bags from her pack for holding the birds in.

"Tell me you didn't hear that Cerulean, Ron?"

Ron, the owner of the centre and birdwatcher extraordinaire, walked along beside her, scanning the nets for birds. He was exactly what someone would picture when they thought 'birdwatcher.' Middle-aged, glasses, head to toe in khaki, with a massive Tilley hat. He had kind eyes beneath his bushy eyebrows that looked like they would get up and crawl off his face at any moment.

He huffed. "Of course I heard it. But seeing a Cerulean isn't more important than getting birds outta these nets. How would you like to be trapped like that?"

Adelia grumbled.

"Why are you even here, Adelia? It's a Saturday morning.

Shouldn't you be nursing a hangover from your wild Friday night with friends instead of hanging out with old farts like me banding birds?"

"Seriously? You think people want to hang out with the weird *bird girl*?"

Because they didn't. Her peers were more interested in boys and booze. She had been labeled weird for as long as she could remember.

I heard she squawks like a bird when she gets really angry.

I heard she has twenty pet birds and even showers with them. How gross.

What a freak.

The rumors she'd heard since she was a kid had made their home in her consciousness. They were inked into her soul like a tattoo, forever reminding her she'd never fit in. And forget about trying to date.

Unless she found a boy who embraced her love of birds and somehow also found joy in waking up at six on a Saturday morning to join her birdwatching—forget it. She was done trying to pretend she was cool.

She didn't need them. Plus, she had her dad. He was, and always would be, her best friend.

Her dad always embraced her love for birds, despite not being a birdwatcher himself. He bought her all the field guides she wanted and despite the fact that birding was obscure for someone her age, he supported her regardless. He would come to help her find the Cerulean Warbler in a heartbeat.

It was just the two of them—and Adelia wouldn't have it any other way. They were a team in everything they did. They had dinner together every night, went hiking on the weekends or hunting for books at the local store down the street. He was a simple man, dedicated to his work and to her.

As a child, she had loved to join him at the soup kitchen on

Sundays, feeling so important when he let her carry the bowls for him, her little legs struggling to keep up as they walked. She still tried to accompany him when she had free time, but he was there every week, regardless, whipping up a batch of his soul-warming minestrone for the regulars.

She thought back to this morning, about how she had woken up after another pitiful night's sleep, dealing with phantom pain. Most of the time it was just phantom sensations, a pins-and-needles type of sensation in a foot that wasn't there, but the odd time it was pain. She'd been dealing with it off and on since the amputation six years ago. Every morning, as part of her routine, she would go to their balcony for some fresh ocean air. The smell of the salt, the crash of the waves—it always helped to clear her thoughts and prepare for the day ahead.

This morning, a small, pointed cough had caused her to turn and find her dad casually leaning against the balcony door, holding a travel mug of coffee. "Forgetting something?" he said with a soft, warm smile.

Yes, some fresh ocean air and dark coffee.

She smiled at him. "Just what I needed."

"It's almost like I know you." He paused for a second. "Bad night again?"

Adelia shoved her hands in her pockets. "It's fine...well, actually, it wasn't, but you know what would make it better? Coming home from work to some cranberry scones." She batted her eyelashes at him.

He laughed. "Anything for you, Addy," he said with a chuckle before stooping to kiss the top of her head. "Now get out of here."

"Love ya, Dad!" she called as she headed out the front door.

"Love you more," he called back.

. . .

SHE KNEW IT WAS RIDICULOUS, but she believed her father was a storybook hero brought to life. He was so true to himself and genuine in everything he did. It shone through in the way he treated the people around him, and she found herself constantly inspired by him. He was everything she hoped to be one day and more.

She would never forget how he held her tight every night for years when she'd come home from school with a tear-stained face after another day of bitchy teenage girls and endless ridicule.

She'd grown up since then, but this side of her—the girl who went traipsing into the woods, brambles in her hair and burrs on her clothes, with binoculars and bird field guide in hand—that was someone only her dad saw now. She was tired of the confused looks and the snide remarks at how strange she was. Maybe one day, she'd find people who cared about her like her dad, but for now, Teilio Larson, part-time chef at the local fish fry and full-time hero, was all she ever needed.

SHE AND RON worked to untangle bird after bird, and Adelia only stopped to pocket some stinging nettle she passed—it was a prickly plant that once handled and cooked appropriately made for a great meal. Maybe she could convince her dad to use it to make nettle soup for dinner. Her mouth watered at the thought. If she was really lucky, she may even convince him to come back with her tomorrow to resume her search for the Cerulean Warbler.

A flutter of wings to the left of her caught her eye as she wandered along. She let out a small gasp as she cautiously approached it.

No flipping way, she thought, stunned at her luck.

It was the Cerulean Warbler she'd been looking for, all tangled up in the net.

It was ruffled as if someone had taken a blow dryer to its feathers and was frantically trying to untangle itself from the net. In its desperate attempt to free itself, it had only managed to twist the cords tighter around its neck. Adelia set to work untangling it.

"Hey, little buddy. How ya doing today?" Yes, she talked to the birds. Maybe the rumours *were* true.

"Hurry up, you useless idiot. Get me out of this damn net." The bird obviously didn't say that, but it seemed like a sassy bird to her. One that would definitely reply like that if it could talk.

It was a breathtaking bird. It was pale blue along its head, back, and wings, which brought to mind delicate forget-me-nots that faded to the colour of freshly fallen snow around its belly. It had a faded black necklace of feathers across its breast, and it peered up at Adelia with an intensity that made her uneasy.

The bird quieted in her hands as she continued untangling. "See? You can tell I'm helping."

As she loosened another knot, she noticed a small metal object attached to the bird's leg.

"What's this?"

Bending over to inspect it closer, she realized it was a tiny, intricate key.

Adelia stepped back for a second and gave the bird a *"what the hell" look,* hoping it would understand. "How did you fly with that attached to your leg? No offense, but you're a pipsqueak."

The bird gave her a definite side-eye.

She pushed the puzzling thought aside for a moment, finished freeing the bird, then bent to gingerly remove the key from its leg. It was delicate but appeared to be made of iron. The top of it was a triangle enclosed in a circle. The triangle was divided into three parts with an intricately sculpted flame sitting atop of it.

Adelia held the key in her palm...it was warm. Its heat settled into her hand, not hot, but like touching a baking pan through a thin oven mitt.

It had an energy to it, like nothing she had encountered before. Uneasiness pooled in the pit of her stomach. This key was no ordinary object. She knew it like she knew how to identify a robin—with absolute certainty and no hesitation.

Adelia pocketed the key in her khakis and glanced at the warbler, still settled in her hand, feeling at odds with herself.

She had an overwhelming sensation to let the bird go without banding it.

"Let me go, let me go." It seemed to chant. She felt the bird's desire to be free so intensely that she swore they were connected telepathically.

It continued to watch her intently, its soulful eyes assessing her unruly blond curls, and she watched it right back.

Suddenly, the meek warbler gained a newfound vigor. It slashed out with its talons at her hands with seemingly impossible strength. It ripped into her palms, splitting the skin and tearing the delicate muscle beneath with a frantic slash.

"Ahh, what the hell!" Her hands exploded in pain and she slackened her grip. The bird took off like a little blue firework into the sky.

Adelia stood there, cradling her bleeding hands, still unsure of what had transpired as she watched the warbler fly farther and farther away.

"I thought we were friends," she mumbled. "Turns out you were just an asshole like everyone else."

Her palms pulsed in pain, as if reminding her that she definitely needed medical attention. The blood pooled in her hands and began to drip onto the soft dirt, colouring it a dark auburn, and she turned to make her way back to the centre for some bandages.

As she did, her thoughts drifted back to the feverish key in her pocket—maybe her dad would know what it was. He always seemed to have answers to her most unexpected questions. And today was turning out to be an unexpected day.

CHAPTER 2

Ron had sent her home with bandages wrapped delicately around her shredded hands and orders to take it easy for the rest of the day. Her hands were throbbing, and she couldn't fathom trying to hold another bird today, let alone inspecting or banding it.

Adelia made her way back across town, watching the hustle and bustle of tourists shopping at surf shops and ice cream joints. The main drag was a dip in the landscape that allowed for sandy beaches to cover the coast.

Their little town was quite the tourist attraction because of it. Adelia swore there was a different fair or carnival in town every weekend that she would beg her dad to come with her to. The magical feeling she got while watching the trapeze artists in particular was her favourite. As a child, she thought they were actually flying through the air like birds. It was as close to actual magic as she could imagine.

"Daddy, are they fairies? Is that how they can fly? Do they have secret wings we can't see?" she had asked him, practically bouncing in her seat.

He had ruffled her blond curls like he always did. "We'll have to ask them after the show. See if they'll give away their secrets."

Adelia had beamed as he continued, "But remember, Addy, fairies and pixies are little." He held his fingers a couple inches apart. "Fae are the ones that are big. They look just like people."

She'd nodded enthusiastically, storing the information away to tell all the girls at school. She had believed fairies and pixies were real for a lot longer than she cared to admit. Which only resulted in more ridicule from kids at school.

After the shows, she would walk with her dad back to their house, chattering about their favourite parts the whole way. They lived on the outskirts of the town, where the land rose high above sea level, and the beachy coastline became cliffs. The jaunt up the hill and out of town to their home was leg-burning and sweat inducing—likely a challenge even if she had two legs. She'd have to clean her socket when she got home. The less sweat build-up down there, the better. Dealing with sores in addition to her hand would not be ideal.

Finally, she made it to the sloping gravel driveway leading up to her quaint two-story house. It sat on a cliff overlooking the ocean, and she could hear the water crashing against the rocks below as she drew closer. Adelia had always been afraid to get close to the edge. With her luck, she'd trip and plummet to the craggy rocks below, then be swept out with the current, never to be found again.

She shivered at the thought.

Instead, sitting on the cobblestone patio curled up in her Adirondack chair with a good book was one of her favourite things in the world. Especially with the lullaby of crashing waves.

As she approached the house, the salty air coating her skin, she noticed the front door was open, which wasn't all that unusual, but it was usually the back doors her dad opened to let the sea breeze in. She walked up to the door and realized it wasn't open, it was off its hinges—completely broken.

She pushed it the rest of the way open. "Dad?" She paused, anxiously anticipating his response. "You home?"

She threw her pack onto the bench in the mudroom and halted mid-step as she noticed all the debris on the floor. Papers scattered the hardwood, and the mirror by the door was shattered. Shards of glass littered the room, like frozen fractals of ice.

"DAD?" she yelled this time.

In a panicked stupor, she staggered into the kitchen, her chest tightening like there was a vice grip around it as she beheld what was in front of her.

Drawing in air became harder.

Blood.

There was blood on the floor.

It splattered the linoleum like a Pollock painting, still wet in the places where it was thickest. It was dark and congealing, and its metallic smell permeated her every pore.

Adelia gagged at the odour and looked around with hesitant eyes. The room was spinning from the shock she felt, and she had to grab the wall to steady herself.

The kitchen looked like a tornado had swept through. The cupboards were ripped open, the contents spilled across the counters and island. The light fixtures were cracked and bright light escaped from their shattered bulbs, casting the space in uneven fragmented light. Baking bowls were strewn across the floor, the mixture for her cranberry scones splattered on the ground. More papers were ripped and shredded throughout the kitchen, now soaking in the blood.

She glanced towards the back door and sucked in a sudden breath.

"Oh God. Oh no." Adelia collapsed to her knees amongst the chaos, hitting the floor with a dull thud.

Massive human-shaped footprints in the wet blood. Twice the size of her dad's. And a smear of blood, like someone had been dragged out of the house.

The world was becoming hazy. It was impossible to think straight or rationalize what was happening.

Nothing made sense. Was it a robbery? Kidnapping? Murder?

Adelia knew one thing for sure.

Her dad was not here anymore. She was alone. And she had no idea where to go from here.

"OKAY, time to call the police. That's what I should be doing," Adelia muttered, reaching into her pocket to pull out her phone with trembling fingers, barely able to hold on to the device as she tried to come to terms with what was happening.

If you had been home, maybe this wouldn't have happened. You could have helped. Calling the police then could have actually saved him. Her constant self-doubt companion chimed in.

The world felt like it was collapsing in on itself, a black hole forming in her chest that threatened to consume her with dark, endless grief.

What if he's actually gone?

What if I walked right into a trap?

What if the culprits are still here?

She shook her head. "No. I can't think like that." Talking out loud to drown out the voices in her head helped her calm down a bit.

Then, a crash echoed from upstairs.

It seemed unnaturally loud in the heavy silence of the

ransacked house. Adelia dove behind the island, breathless, her heart beating so fast, she might as well be running a marathon.

There were two options; either call the police and stay hidden down here, or head upstairs and see what the noise was. It could very well be her dad. Maybe he fought off the robbers already? Or was he in the middle of doing so and needed help?

That had to be it.

Convinced that it was her father upstairs in his room, wanting to believe it *so* badly that it became the most plausible reality in her delirium, Adelia made her decision.

She wasn't in a TV drama or movie. Nothing like this happened in real life, her shell-shocked brain tried to convince her. Her dad was strong and resourceful. He was undoubtedly fine.

In the back of her mind, she knew it was stupid, but something pulled her upstairs like she was a puppet on a string. It was a call to action. She had a mysterious tether on her heart, tugging her towards an unknown fate.

Her feet moved of their own accord, but some part of her registered the cast iron pan on the stovetop. She grabbed it, wielding it like a sword.

I saw this in a movie once, and it worked pretty well. No harm in being cautious, she rationalized.

She adjusted her footing to imitate how she moved through the forest and crept her way through the empty house, around the debris. She moved as if she were made of wind.

Adelia focused on one step at a time, trying to push the picture of the blood-soaked kitchen from her mind with each step up the stairs, closer to the sounds of shuffling.

The world began to shift back into focus as she summited the stairs and paused outside her room, where the sounds were coming from. Straining her ears, she heard faint rustling around as if someone was sifting through the drawers. The footsteps in the room were soft, and the door was open a crack, enough for Adelia to steal a look into the room.

The person in the room was most definitely *not* her father.

It was a young man around her age. He was searching flippantly through the drawer, flicking aside its contents with careless movement. He wore all leather, black as a starless winter night. It was partially covered by a cloak of a matching shade that drifted down below his knees, with a tall collar. The cloak was trimmed with an intricate gold pattern along the breast, where the buttons met, and along the cuffs. There was also a curious golden emblem on the breast that she couldn't make out from where she was. He was wearing gloves that were made of the same leather, but cracked and worn, which contrasted his immaculate appearance.

Adelia could only see his side profile, but he was tall, lean, and rather well built. He moved with precision and purpose as he deftly scanned the drawers with long fingers, clearly searching for something.

His hair was what caught her eye, though—it was a light smokey grey that reminded her of the colour of mist that blanketed the beaches in the early morning. It was short around the ears and shaggier at the top, giving it a tousled "I just climbed out of bed" look. He absent-mindedly brushed it from his eyes and paused. He seemed to find something in the drawer and smirked to himself about whatever was in there.

What in the world is he doing?

Wait a second. Adelia's train of thought stalled, and pure horror flooded her thoughts. She could feel her cheeks turning scarlet.

That's my underwear drawer.

Adelia whirled around, her back softly connecting with the wood-paneled wall.

She was unsure whether to be embarrassed or angry.

No.

Definitely angry.

She peeked back around the corner to take a closer look at the intruder and noticed the blood staining his clothes. It was splattered across his cloak garishly.

Her own blood boiled and clouded her vision as anger bubbled up inside her. There was a random stranger in *her* house, sifting through *her* clothes, splattered with what *had* to be her father's blood.

In her newly fevered state, she gripped the pan tighter until her fingers went white, adrenaline coursing through her veins. She could feel her heart pounding against her ribs as though it was a bird in a cage. Her hands trembled from both fear and her now brewing anger. Before she could think twice about what she was about to do, she thrust open the door and in two long strides had reached him.

She swung her homebrew battle-ax at his head with more might than she ever thought possible. It was as if her dad was there with her and his hands were on the handle with hers, adding to her strength. The pan connected with his temple, and a sickening thud echoed across the room. The force of the blow reverberated back through the handle into Adelia's hands and up her arms. It stung her palms from the injury earlier and momentarily distracted her before the stranger crumpled to the ground with a look of disbelief and bewilderment in his eyes. A trickle of blood leaked onto the floor, dyeing his light hair a dark, vicious red.

Of the two of them, Adelia thought she might be the more stunned at the outcome of her actions. She now had an unconscious man lying bleeding at her feet, a house in ruins, a missing father, and only a frying pan as an ally. As she came back to reality, she realized the stupidity of what she had just done.

Holy shit. What the hell do I do now? I just assaulted someone.

She had never been one to think things through. Her grandfather always told her she was foolish and never took the time to think before she acted. Clearly, he had been right. She had to stop acting impulsively. She silently chided herself.

She set to work, grabbing some of her scarves from the closet and meticulously tying his hands behind his back. At the very least she could incapacitate this intruder and call for the authorities. Luckily, her dad had taught her how to tie a proper knot, like a sailor working on the high seas. He had always made sure she knew necessary survival skills, especially since she spent so much time in the woods alone. She could set a snare, start a fire, and even skin a rabbit if she needed. Being an amputee had never stopped her from living her life to the fullest.

She scooted back to admire her work. Soft silk scarves dug into his skin slightly, but before she had a chance to double-check her work, he groaned arduously.

He sluggishly raised his head, as if the haze clouding his vision was slowly lifting. He sat up and tried to flick his grey hair out of his eyes but winced at the sudden motion.

Adelia figured she had probably given him a concussion. He slowly scanned the room and caught sight of Adelia still crouching on the ground behind him like a bird on a wire.

She had grossly underestimated her strength, it seemed. Miraculously, he was already conscious.

His dark shadowed eyes appraised her, hesitating briefly on her face and ears, then settling on her heavily bandaged hands that were now seeping scarlet through the gauze. She cursed as she realized the unhinged swinging of the pan had caused the wounds to resume bleeding. She wiped her hands on her pants, leaving streaks of bright red before she realized it wasn't the same as wiping her greasy fingers after eating her dad's fish and chips. Blood wouldn't come out so easily.

Shit.

An emotion that looked eerily like concern tinged his eyes for a moment, but it quickly evaporated into exasperation.

He cocked an eyebrow at her, looking completely comfortable lying on his back with his hands bound. "Would you like to enlighten me as to what is going on?"

She blinked. That was not what she expected. Adelia was convinced he would be angry or try to threaten her, not act like the innocent one. She realized with growing outrage, he had said it like *she* was the one who needed to explain herself.

She drew herself up to her full height, lacking though it was, inflated her chest with a subtle, sharp intake of air, and side-stepped around to face him.

Up close, he was all angles, sharp cheekbones, and a defined jaw. He was looking at her with an annoying smugness, like he knew she was out of her depth despite how well she thought she was faking it.

At least he can't see that he's tied up with scarves, she thought, relieved.

His hair had fallen over his eyes again, and he delicately twisted his head to fling it away. That's when Adelia caught a glimpse of pointed ears as his hair swept past his face.

Confusion washed over her like the waves on the rocks below them.

"So, Goldilocks, are you ready to tell me who you are? And why you have me tied up with silk scarves? Not that I don't like it." He smirked again.

Shit.

"*Me?* You are the one in *my* house, rooting through *my* room, with blood on your clothes," she said boldly, not sure if her shaking hands were from the after effect of hitting him with the pan or nerves.

Unaffected by her scolding, he proceeded to evaluate her

entirely now as he slowly sat up. It was as if he could read exactly what was going on behind her eyes. He saw the fear, the uncertainty, and she realized he was going to try and use that to his advantage.

He sighed as if having to explain this was a hassle. "All right, we both know you have no idea what's going on. I recommend you untie me. I'll be on my way, and you can go back to doing whatever it is humans do."

Humans? What does that even mean?

"No way, Santa Claus," she flung back at him and internally winced. Comebacks were never her forte, and she knew the comparison to the fat, jolly, old man was far from accurate. He was poised, handsome, and his smirk held a promise of something wicked lurking beneath. His grey hair was the colour of craters on the moon, breathtakingly ethereal. Adelia figured she *should* be afraid of him, but some part of her was intrigued.

She looked around for the frying pan but saw it lying behind him, and she was hesitant to get that close to him to grab it. Instead, she swiftly covered her hand with her sweater sleeve as protection and reached delicately into her pocket and drew out the stinging nettle she had been saving in there for dinner. She held it out like a rapier, inches from his face. "Now, you're going to tell me what you're doing here."

He looked at the plant, a crooked smile twisting the corner of his lips. Then he burst out laughing. He continued to chuckle at her leaf sword and said, with disbelief in his voice, "What? You plan on attacking me with a flower?"

Well, he's right. This might not have been the most frightening thing I could have done, but I have to roll with it now. So much for thinking things through.

Adelia narrowed her eyes and growled, "I said... tell me what you know." And she thrust the plant into his face.

Stinging nettle was generally harmless, but it's stems and

leaves had thousands of tiny hairs on them, and when those came in contact with the skin, it was like getting stabbed with a thousand tiny burning needles laced with venom. The intense reaction only lasted for a few minutes, but the initial intensity was still fierce.

He was still laughing when the plant connected with his face, and the leaves brushed the inside of his mouth. He sputtered in disgust and spat the leaves back out onto his lap with a wet splat. He looked less than impressed at her.

Wait for it, Adelia thought.

And then…

Horror and pain flashed behind his eyes as the chemicals started to sink into his skin and the burning started.

"What in the Orb's name. Why is my face on fire? What the fuck did you do to me?"

He struggled against his bonds, shaking his head as if he could shake off the feeling of burning that would be spreading across his face and mouth. Adelia knew it would build in intensity as the minutes dragged on. She had only ever brushed up against the plant while walking and had the needles pierce her leg. She couldn't imagine getting a mouthful of them.

It was Adelia's turn for a smug look. Clearly, he didn't know what this plant was or what its effects were. She could continue to use it to her advantage to get him to talk.

He was swearing quite loudly now, still trying to free his hands and rub his face on his shoulder in desperation.

Then, her bedroom door was thrown open with a resounding bang that shook the room.

Three more strangers stood there.

Pointed ears, beautiful faces, and with more weapons than Adelia could count.

CHAPTER 3

"What the hell is going on?" the girl leading the group roared.

Adelia's head snapped towards her, quickly assessing the figures now occupying the doorway.

In the foreground, a dark-skinned girl stood assertively with both hands on her hips, wearing the same leather gear as the boy. Her hair was various shades of blue, with long bangs that swept across her face covering one eye. The entire left side of her head was shaved, and the rest of her hair was swept into a tangled bun on her head. Her eyes had a wicked gleam to them, almost as much as the duel swords criss-crossed against her back. She had daggers hooked along her belt, and she radiated a cool, calm, coordinated energy.

She glanced between Adelia and the boy.

Adelia, who was standing holding a leafy plant at his face, and the boy sitting on the floor tied up with scarves, a scarlet rash now blooming across his face.

It was quite the scene to behold, she thought belatedly.

The boy she had attacked spoke first. "Novak, I can explain," he said coldly, regaining his composure as if he wasn't just losing it over a plant. "This girl—she attacked me. I don't know how she snuck up—"

Cutting him off mid-sentence, a massive surge of water exploded into the room. It swept from where the blue-haired girl was standing, knocking Adelia down and sweeping the boy towards the wall. His spine collided with the dresser, causing it to splinter from the force. He let out a groan from the impact.

The water filled the room ankle-deep, soaking the bed-skirt and the bottom shelf of the bookcase.

It was shockingly cold, stealing the breath from Adelia as she tumbled backward with the force of it. It was like she had fallen into freezing glacier water, her skin already numb and tingling.

She attempted to regain her balance and stand up quickly, thanking the higher powers that she was wearing her waterproof leg today, but found all the water now rushing towards her unnaturally, as if it were alive. She took a startled step back into the wall behind her and realized there was nowhere to go as the water rushed like rapids down the river that was her bedroom floor.

"What is going on?" she screamed wildly.

Before the water reached her, she threw up her hands to shield herself from the crushing impact. Then it changed course and shot upwards. The water rushed towards the ceiling, becoming reverse waterfalls of iridescent turquoise water.

Then, as quickly as it occurred, the water froze in place, halting as if time stood still.

And Adelia found herself standing in a cage of ice.

Stray droplets, now frozen, plinked to the ground and shattered like glass. The cage's bars were thick, jagged ice, reaching to the ceiling like frozen stalagmites.

Panicked, she grabbed hold of the serrated bars in front of her, only to snatch them back instantly. This ice was not just freezing; it was as cold and unforgiving as liquid nitrogen, leaving her bandaged hands covered in frost. Had it not been for the bandages, her hands would have been ice-burned.

She exhaled, her breath forming an ephemeral white cloud around her.

The smokey-haired boy groaned and clutched his stomach in pain. He slowly stood up and cast a side-eye glance at the girl named Novak. "What was that for?"

"Sorry. I'd say I had to, but in reality I just didn't want to hear your excuses." She didn't seem sorry at all or concerned that a violent tsunami had flooded the room moments ago.

Adelia was convinced she must have hit her head. There was nothing rational about what was going on right now. She tried to poke the bars of ice again to make sure they were real.

Solid ice. Very much *real* ice.

This can't seriously be happening.

"Well?" Novak continued, "Do you want to explain why you were tied up on the floor, Ash?" She made her way over to him and began to untie his hands roughly.

For some reason, Adelia blurted out, "He was looking through my underwear!"

As if that explained anything, she chided herself. There were more pressing issues at hand.

The boy named Ash snapped his eyes to her. She noticed they were a warm caramel colour, with thick lashes that brushed his cheeks as he blinked. His expression was challenging to read. Was that guilt or amusement in those shadowed eyes?

Novak blinked slowly, looking back at Ash. "And... did you find anything?"

"No, nothing of importance." He stole a glance at Adelia as he stood up and gave her a sly wink. "I think I was searching through her room by accident. I don't think this is the right place." He shrugged.

Adelia swore she saw the ghost of a smirk.

"Well then, I guess we have to take care of the girl. We can't have loose ends," she replied coldly. She turned to go, smoothly spinning on her heels on the damp hardwood, and pushed her way through the two other strangers standing in the doorway.

Panic flooded over Adelia like the water over her feet moments ago. This had escalated so quickly. How could she have possibly thought that she had this under control? There was clearly something going on, and she was way out of her league. She was trapped inside a cage of ice in her own bedroom, her father was missing, and these strangers were going to murder her. What else could *take care of the girl* mean?

Following Novak's lead, one of the strangers in the doorway began to leave and the other one held back. He was tall and significantly bulkier than the rest, his muscled arms visible beneath the thick fabric of his clothes. His long midnight hair was swept back in a knot at his nape, accentuating his sharp jawline and broad shoulders. His features were distinctly Asian in quality. There was a shield strapped to his back and held himself with a silent surety. When he stepped towards Adelia, she suddenly thought his features made him look very inhuman.

Actually, all of them were similar in that sense. Adelia noticed the way they all moved, like they were feline; graceful, yet strong.

She may not know who these people were, or what they were, but she did know she wouldn't be going down without a fight.

Her dad had always affirmed to her that she was a strong, capable young woman who could fend for herself. She no longer had the frying pan, but her binoculars were still strung across her shoulder. Hitting someone with those would probably hurt a bit at least, maybe give her a chance to escape. She tried to hold onto this flicker of hope and not let it go like she did the Cerulean Warbler this morning.

With determination in her eyes, she looked at the large man with the bun approaching and said, "Don't you *dare* touch me." She could hear how cold her voice was, unyielding like the ice around her.

Oh God, this boy was *huge* up close. A skyscraper of a man.

He faltered at her words, guilt dusting his features momentarily before she continued.

"Someone is going to tell me what is going on here. My father is missing, my kitchen is covered in blood, and I am locked in a cage of ice! It was supposed to be a good day today! I saw a damn Cerulean Warbler!" she screamed.

All four strangers paused at this statement and exchanged an unreadable look. Novak strode toward the cage gracefully, pushing her way past the others until she was standing on the other side of the bars.

"Is your father Teilio Larson?" she asked, brows furrowing together.

"Uhh, yes? How do you know him?" she replied, shocked at the familiarity with which she spoke his name.

"Well, make me Molten and throw me in the lava." She barked a laugh and turned to her companions. "Team, looks like this isn't the wrong place after all. We have our first lead. And a Wind."

"There is no possible way," replied the boy Novak had called Ash. "She's just a plain human girl." He approached the cage, and Adelia wished she still had the nettle with her. His face was returning to a normal colour now, but his eyes glinted with cold anger. Clearly, he wasn't impressed that he had been humiliated in front of his team.

"I'll give it to you that she's a feisty little thing. But we still have no use for her. We can get her to give us some information and then be on our way. We're running out of time." He glanced out the window towards the ocean as if he could see something transpiring far off the coast. Adelia followed his gaze, but all she saw was the sun reaching its peak in a cloudless sky.

The enormous boy with the bun finally spoke up, his voice thick and rough. "If her dad is Teilio, then she has to be a Wind, right?"

Novak squinted at Adelia thoughtfully. "She must be."

"What is a Wind?" she ground out. Her patience was wearing thin.

Skyscraper man replied, looking so excited, like a kid on Christmas. Weirdly enough, the warm expression suited him. "Get ready for a bomb to be dropped. You're Fae."

CHAPTER 4

"*Ha. Ha. Ha.* Very funny," Adelia mocked.

The group around her didn't laugh. They were looking at her expectantly.

"You can't be serious," Adelia sputtered out. It was laughable. Her? Fae? The magical creatures she read about in books as a child?

Novak continued, taking over for the muscular boy. "It's a lot more than we have time to explain. But your dad, Teilio, was a well-known soldier in the Wind King's army. If you're his daughter, as you claim, then that also makes you a Fae, specifically from the Wind Court. I'm assuming maybe someone used magic on you to hide it—since you look human."

She's speaking gibberish, Adelia thought.

Novak continued, not waiting for Adelia to gather her thoughts, "Your dad created a gate and key over fifteen years ago during the Molten War to lock away the members of the Molten Court for the Wind King. He was a powerful Fae, one of the King's best. But over time, the gate has begun to collapse.

The Molten are escaping, and we are here to fix that. And to do that, we need to find him."

Adelia's mind was reeling, overwhelmed with information. Her father, a soldier? But he was a chef. He had never told her anything about fighting in a war. Betrayal washed over her as she tried to comprehend her father's secret life. She thought they were a team, that they told each other everything.

She told him everything.

"Why do you want to find him exactly?" she said.

"He disappeared after he used the key over fifteen years ago, clearly far away from Faerie." She glanced around the room with disgust, as if her father couldn't have chosen a less attractive location to relocate. "You see, we were losing the war, so he used the key before it was ready. If he hadn't, the Molten likely would have demolished the Wind Court and moved on to all the others next. But because he used it improperly, it didn't seal the gate fully, so it's breaking now. And the King is angry. We assume he fled out of fear of the King's wrath."

She shrugged. "With the Molten rising in power again due to the increase in volcanic activity here, and the gate breaking, we need the key to fix it. Now. Your father fled with the key and no one has been able to locate it since. The key has become an enigma. An object coveted by the Wind King and the Molten for two very different reasons. And now that the gate is breaking, well, a few strong Molten have escaped their banishment and are looking for both your dad and the key. But we," she said, gesturing to her team, "are part of the Faerie Guard, protectors of all the courts. Our job is to stop the Molten Fae."

The world seemed to slow around her, and a roaring began in Adelia's ears that blocked out the sound of Novak's voice. The small key she had forgotten about in her pocket suddenly felt twice as heavy. She could feel the heat from the little key sitting in there, burning a hole through her pants.

Could the key they were searching for be the same one she found this morning? It seemed too coincidental.

"What happens when you find the key?" She was beyond curious to find out more from the blue-haired girl despite her better judgement. She vaguely remembered that she was still trapped in a cage, and this girl had been about to off her before finding out Teilio was her dad. But despite Adelia's apprehension and absolute disbelief, she was drawn to the mysterious mythical world being described. Another world? Fae? There was no way.

"We use the key to seal the gate again, and we will retrieve it no matter what." Novak looked determined. As if succeeding in this task mattered more to her than Adelia knew. Her muscles were taut, standing like a real soldier, with rigid posture and confident chin tilt.

Adelia ran through the information she had gathered so far. They were Fae. They needed to stop a war with a magical key. They only needed her dad because they had no idea where he had hidden this key. They seemed to have little concern for him or his safety. They would focus on finding this key. He was a pawn, someone they needed to use and then toss aside once they had it.

All this information was making it sound like she was likely correct in her first assumption that her dad was truly gone—and not of his own free will, she realized with growing dread. Could he have been kidnapped by these Molten Fae?

Adelia was unsure what to make of the Fae around her, though. The whole idea seemed laughable—that Fae existed, let alone that she might be one of them? She also didn't know whether she should trust them or not. Right now, she was leaning towards not. Not until she was out of this cage and had more answers.

Adelia observed their matching uniforms, the weapons on

their belts. The daggers and swords visible were shiny and well-kept. She wondered what else these Faerie Guards were responsible for other than tracking down magical keys from soldiers who had defected. Who were these Molten people? Were they actually bad? Frankly, Adelia thought trapping an entire group of people behind a gate forever sounded a lot more like a crime, not some act of heroism and bravery.

All she knew right now was that if this was all true, it seemed that her father's dark past may have gotten him into trouble. She certainly wasn't quite ready to accept that part, but she couldn't deny the fact that her dad was missing, and she wasn't going to wait around, hoping he'd come back. Or leave his fate to the hands of these *Fae*. He had always been there for her—it was her turn to be there for him.

All she had to do was convince these guards to take her with them.

She could make sure his safety and rescue, if need be, were a priority. She might not be a magical soldier, but she could make sure these guards didn't screw over her dad, and she could do her best to try and hold them accountable. The only problem was how to convince them she wasn't useless.

She didn't have to actually trust them.

If she played her cards right, they would find her dad and she could learn more about these Fae.

She just had to plead her case well.

"So, what you're telling me is that you have no leads at all right now—other than me. I'm the only one who knows my dad well enough to know where he might go, who he talks to, and where he possibly hid this key. And you have me locked up in a cage." She crossed her arms and leaned back against the wall behind her, feigning a confidence she definitely didn't feel. "Doesn't seem like a good plan on your part. Some Faerie Guard you all are."

. . .

A FEW MINUTES LATER, Adelia was sitting downstairs in her kitchen, the mysterious group now sitting on the barstools around her kitchen island. The blood on the floor was disconcerting, so she attempted to avert her gaze from the congealing mess behind her. She found that breathing through her mouth helped to mask the smell.

Upstairs moments ago, Novak had quickly nodded to the fourth member of her group, who had then made the ice cage dissolve into a cloud of snow, which covered Adelia's hair in fine white crystals. She was starting to believe they might actually be Fae because what she had witnessed so far had no other logical explanation. So far, she had deduced that the leader of the group, Novak, must have some sort of water power, and the other girl must have control over snow somehow.

Adelia eyed Ash, with his light grey hair, and tried to imagine what power he might have. He hadn't attacked her with anything when they were upstairs, but she had caught him pretty off guard. Maybe he had snow powers too. It would certainly match his hair.

Once downstairs, Adelia had decided to make tea. It was more for herself, to warm her icy fingers and calm her turbulent nerves, but she had tentatively offered it to the others as a peace offering. She needed them to trust her, so that she could get more information. Skyscraper man was the only one who took the mug with a smile.

Introductions had followed. Novak, the blue-haired girl, was indeed in charge of the small group, having been a member of this mysterious elite Faerie Guard for years. Skyscraper man with the bun was Rory, and Maewyn was the other girl. She was a delicate creature with hair the colour of frost on a window pane, pearlescent skin, and icy blue eyes. She looked as fragile as a snowflake, completely out of place among the other three.

Finally, there was Ash.

He was sitting with his arms crossed, staring at the tea in front of him, tendrils of stream sending a faint aroma of peppermint into the air. He looked about as pleased as if she had given him a cup of curdled milk.

Why is he so pissed off? Adelia wondered. Yes, she had gotten the upper hand on him, but was he that misogynistic that he'd hold a grudge against her for it? Or maybe it had nothing to do with her and it was the fact that *anyone* had gotten an upper hand on him. He looked like the type of guy who always got his way. He had made some flirty comments at first, but as soon as Novak had released Adelia and said they might need her, his mood had flipped.

On top of all of this, a small arctic fox had appeared at Maewyn's side once they got downstairs. It had white fur the shade of Maewyn's hair and had casually snuggled up against her leg once they had all sat down. Adelia figured it must be a pet. She glanced around, and none of the other guards appeared to have one. This whole experience was getting weirder and weirder, but she had to focus if she wanted to get some answers.

Novak had decided they were going to start walking through her dad's last moves before he disappeared, as well as making a list of his friends they might track down.

"So, tell me why I should trust you all?" Adelia inquired skeptically.

All she knew about them was that they were a part of some Faerie Guard, and they were looking for a key to stop some evil Fae from starting a war. They seemed to know a lot about her dad, especially when all she knew was that he was missing. She had no reason to trust what they were saying, especially when it sounded so far-fetched.

Novak's eyes darkened as she spoke. "I promise you that as soon as you see a Molten Fae, you'll be convinced. We want nothing more than to stop them, and the only way we can do that is with your help. We've been searching for some time now for any leads on your dad, a solution on how to fix the gate, the location of the key, *anything*. You're the first solid lead we've had."

Adelia surveyed them all and decided they didn't *look* evil. But then again, neither did Kristy Summers in third grade, who had tripped Adelia and shoved dirt into her mouth one day. The teachers hadn't even believed that docile little Kristy had done such a thing. They had chalked it up to Adelia having tripped and fallen face-first, since she was always looking up instead of at her feet. She shrugged the thought off—yes, she'd remain wary of these people.

"Okay, then tell me more about this key," Adelia asked. She could feel the comforting warmth of the tea snaking through her, slightly easing the ache in her chest that had gripped her since walking in the front door.

This time, Maewyn spoke. Her voice matched her figure, high-pitched and childlike. "Well, the key was originally forged by your father during the Molten War. Basically, Faerie is divided into four main courts: Molten, Terrain, Aqua, and Wind. The key was designed to keep the Molten Fae confined to their court," she said hurriedly.

She didn't speak like she was in a rush, but like she had too many thoughts for her mouth to keep up with. "The key is nothing fancy! Just a small metal key with the symbol of the Molten Court on the top. It kind of looks like a volcano with a star on top of it. See anything like that around?"

She hoped her guilt wasn't showing on her face as she said, "No, I've never seen anything like that before." She prayed the others hadn't noticed her nervous fidgeting or the lack of eye contact. Adelia had never been one to lie—her dad could always read it on her face the moment she tried.

"That's ok! You'd know it if you saw it. I've obviously never gotten to see it, but I heard it is actually hot. Like it's holding so much magical energy that it radiates heat."

Shit.

This is *actually the same key. No denying it now.*

There is absolutely no way I can tell them.

Ash sighed exceptionally loud. "Forget it, Mae. She clearly doesn't know anything."

"Seriously, what's your problem?" Adelia blurted out. He was being unnecessarily rude.

He shrugged. "I just don't think we should be wasting our time trying to explain to some useless human what's going on. It's a waste of time and air."

A waste of air. She was a waste of air.

Freak.

Loser.

Useless.

The words clanged around in her head again and her heart lurched. Ash could go jump off the cliff. He didn't matter either. The only thing that mattered was finding her dad. If she were to give up this key, it would all be over. She would never find out more about the Fae, and more importantly, she would likely never see her dad again. She had no delusions that she could do this alone. Hell, she didn't even know how to get to this Faerie place, and never seeing her father again wasn't an option despite the secrets he had kept from her. When it came to family, that's what mattered most.

She could pretend.

She could lie.

She would use them and do whatever she needed to save her father.

CHAPTER 5

Cupboards.
Desks.
Under couches and in closets.
In every cup and behind every painting.
Novak searched it all.

Around and around the house she stormed, in case Teilio had hidden the key here. Adelia played along, feigning ignorance, and helped them search. It was the most elaborate game of hot and cold ever, and every time Novak neared Adelia, she waited with bated breath to see if Novak would be able to sense the key.

She never did.

"How is there nothing here? I thought for sure he'd hide it here!" Novak was so exasperated, visible steam was coming out of her ears. *Real steam*, like a cartoon come to life.

Adelia watched, dumbstruck.

"Uhh, you got..." She pointed lamely to her ears.

Novak lifted her hand and jolted at the liquid pouring out.

"Ugh, sorry, side effect of being Aqua Fae. Rory!" she called to the kitchen. "Get me some more of that hot, calming fluid, stat!"

"On it, boss!" Rory called back gruffly.

Novak and Adelia made their way to the dining room and everyone else joined, Rory with another cup of tea in his hands for Novak, which she took with a small nod. Ash moved to glance at some of the photographs framed on the old hutch, while the others sank down onto the old oak chairs, dejected.

Adelia followed Ash's gaze as he browsed the frames. There was one of Adelia as an infant, posed in a frilly dress and matching socks, with a lopsided smile and chubby cheeks. Another of her dad and her on a birding trip, binoculars around their necks, her dad wearing a cheesy tourist shirt from their trip out east that said 'Stud Puffin'. He paused at the next photograph of Teilio with his arm around another man. They had their drinks raised in cheers and smiles on their faces.

Ash picked up the photo and turned it to face Adelia. "Who's this?"

Adelia stood up and looked at the photograph he was holding. "That's my uncle Tad. Well, I call him my uncle. He's one of my dad's oldest friends."

"And where does your uncle Tad live?"

Adelia paused. He had only ever visited them here, and she never questioned it. They lived on the beach, and staying here was a mini-vacation for most people. "Uhh, I actually don't know... we never went to visit him..."

He picked up the frame and held it up to the rest of his team. He looked derisively at Adelia, like she was proving herself unhelpful and this was a colossal waste of time. "Look familiar?" he asked, his voice thick with annoyance.

Maewyn jumped to her feet and slammed her delicate hands down on the table. "That's Tadriel Winspur!"

He gave a pointed look at Novak. "We can do this without

her, Novak. Let's go. I don't know how Rory missed these photographs when he was *supposed to* be searching down here earlier, but either way, we can head back now. I know where to look for Tadriel. He might know where Teilio is."

Rory, who had gone over to the fridge and now had his head buried inside, looked out, offended.

"I promise I looked at those. I got distracted looking at the one with the girl who had all this purple around her eyes." He motioned over his eyelids. "I guess that was you?" He looked over at Adelia.

She glanced over at the hutch and cringed. It was her grade eight graduation photo that her dad had insisted on keeping. In the picture she was sporting braces, pigtails, and gaudy purple eyeshadow all the way up to her eyebrows. At the time, she had thought it was fashionable and very mature.

"It's makeup," she huffed.

Rory strode over to the picture again to inspect it. "You look like you have two black eyes."

Adelia threw her hands up. "Oh, come on! That's just mean. It was very stylish at the time."

"I doubt that," Ash quipped and Adelia threw him a derisive look.

"Humans are weird," Rory grumbled.

"Technically, she isn't human!" Maewyn piped in.

Novak shook her head at the derailment in conversation and looked back at Ash. "I hate this situation as much as you, Ash, but this girl might actually end up being useful." Her eyes burned a deep blue like the dark depthless ocean, and she leaned back in her chair with an air of authority. "And since you refuse to use your powers, maybe having an actual Wind Fae with us could come in handy." Venom and anger coated her words. The words were like poisoned barbs that hit their target the moment she spoke them.

Anger flashed across Ash's features. He dropped the picture carelessly back onto the hutch and stormed out of the room without another word.

A heavy silence followed his exit, the tension palpable in the air. Adelia stood still beside the now broken glass of the frame, holding her breath.

She wasn't sure what had just happened, but Novak thought she might be useful.

Did that mean they were going to take her with them? If so, it was exactly what she had been hoping for. The only obstacle being Ash. He seemed to be against her helping in any capacity, let alone coming with them. But she could be quite convincing when she wanted to. Hopefully, he'd be back from his temper tantrum soon. She wondered what Novak had meant when she had said he refused to use his Wind powers.

Maewyn sat back down softly into her worn chair. "Let's get back to work," she said, eyes downcast.

FOR THE NEXT FEW HOURS, the group sat around her small oak dining table, discussing her father. Countless more cups of tea were consumed and bags of Cheetos that Rory couldn't get enough of.

"The crisp! The cheese!" He shoved another handful into his mouth—and given his size that was a lot of Cheetos. Adelia struggled to avoid smiling. She wasn't supposed to like these guys.

As he munched, they reviewed all of Teilio's last locations and any friends he had here. They looked through his journals and mail for any clues.

They found nothing.

Adelia had to keep reminding herself not to feel guilty about sending them on a wild goose chase for a key she had in her pocket.

"We'll find it. I know we will." Novak seemed absolutely convinced they would figure it out. Like the information in front of her was a puzzle, and she just had to put all the pieces together. Determination shone in her eyes, and despite the failure to find any more clues, her resolve never faltered.

Rory, however, was losing steam. He slumped into a chair with a sigh. "I really don't think we are going to find it here, Novak."

She raised her eyebrows at him incredulously. "Not with that attitude, we aren't."

He let his head loll back off the chair dramatically. "Of course. We haven't even checked inside the toilets yet."

Novak paused. "Do humans hide things there?"

Rory stole a glance at Adelia and she stifled a smirk. Without waiting for his answer, Novak stormed off to the bathrooms. As soon as she was out of earshot, Maewyn smacked Rory on the shoulder.

"You shouldn't be messing with her right now!" she hissed.

He shrugged. "Sorry, I needed a minute to breathe. I admire her determination, but I don't think we're going to find it here."

"Hmm. You're probably right, but let's keep looking with her until Ash comes back at least," Maewyn responded.

No one had bothered to go look for him, so Adelia figured Novak's earlier comment must have really hit a nerve, or storming off was normal for him. It was like they were all giving him time to cool off.

She found herself wondering about what his powers were and why he didn't use them. Based on the few feats she saw from Novak and Maewyn, it seemed absurd to refuse to use them. The way Novak had phrased her jab had made it seem like Ash was a Wind Fae too.

Like her.

She was a *Fae*.

The thought hadn't quite sunk in yet, the mere idea of having powers so daunting, it was hard to absorb.

Everything in her rational mind screamed at her that it was all a dream, but she couldn't deny what she had seen earlier.

Fae were real.

CHAPTER 6

ASH

Ash stormed away from Novak and the others without a glance back. He made a show of slamming the front door to drive his point home. He didn't care they thought he was having a fit. It irked him to know Novak still harboured resentment at him for choosing to fight without magic.

He'd shown her time and time again he was an asset to this team with his sword. How many Fae even *owned*, let alone knew how to wield a magical sword? He'd like to see how they fared without him. The others were best at fighting from a distance with their powers. But if their enemy got up close and personal? Yeah, not as convenient to rely on powers. That's what he was for. That's why they were a team. Where one of them lacked, another made up for.

Ash sighed and sat down at the edge of the cliff behind Adelia's house. He dangled his feet precariously over the ledge and watched the waves crash below.

He took his sword off his back and laid it down beside him. Even in the bright afternoon sun, it shone white and angelic. It was filled with pure magic. Straight from the Orb itself. He took another calming breath and decided they'd be fine inside if he killed some time out here instead. He should cool off a bit before going back to help.

He hated to admit this place was actually quite scenic.

His home in the Wind Court was breathtaking, but the sheer drop of this cliff and the ocean below were like nothing he'd seen before. Fae didn't come to the human world. Yes, there were gates, but why would a Fae *want* to come here? He had been told the human world was boring, ugly, and filled with small-minded humans. He was beginning to wonder if there was more to this world, though.

He sighed and lay down to stare up at the sky. He couldn't wrap his head around why Novak was convinced they needed this random girl. Yes, she was Teilio's daughter, but they had learned the hard way not to trust strangers. And what did she have to bring to the team anyway? She might technically be Fae, but she grew up in the human world. She knew nothing of her powers, of Faerie or the Molten.

And they were running out of time.

They didn't need her help. Adelia could stay here on her pretty little cliff and go back to being oblivious about Faerie. They couldn't afford anyone slowing them down. *He* couldn't afford anyone slowing him down. It was clear she has no idea where her dad is—that much was obvious. And now that they had a lead with Tadriel, there was no need to bring her along.

Not to mention that he didn't *want* anyone else tagging along.

Dax had left, their team was down to four, and that was fine by him.

The others were dependable, loyal, and he trusted them with his life. There was no way he was trusting Adelia after knowing her for an hour. There was no doubt she'd end up holding them back and endanger them all. And she would most definitely get in the way of his own goals.

Finding this key was imperative. If the Molten escaped, they would burn everything to the ground. Queen Karai's fury would know no bounds. They wanted revenge for being locked away and he couldn't even blame them. But they couldn't escape.

He wouldn't—*he couldn't*—lose everything again.

It might just break him.

Ash fisted his hands and took a deep breath in his nose and out his mouth. There was really nothing he wouldn't do to succeed.

He lost track of how much time elapsed out there on the cliff before he saw a flash to his left...right where the gate to Faerie was.

Had the commander of the Orb sent more guards to assist them here? Why the hell did no one think they had this under control? Ash grabbed his sword and stood up.

Except when he whirled around to lose it on some guards for interfering with his mission, instead he saw a monstrous figure barreling towards the house.

Fuck.

He darted after it, pumping his arms and sprinting at top speed. But even at his considerable height, its strides were twice as long.

He screamed at the others to get out, but the waves drowned out his voice.

How can this happen?

How the hell is it here?

CHAPTER 7

After what felt like an eternity of fruitless searching with Novak, a loud crash came from the main entrance hall in the direction Ash had stormed off. The abrupt cacophonous sound of colliding metal reverberated through the house. Novak leapt to her feet in an instant. All three Fae were rushing towards the door before Adelia had even left her chair. She hurriedly followed the guards but halted as she rounded the corner and the open doorway came into view.

A person was standing there.

Or what resembled the vague shape of a person.

It had black hair that looked like it was disintegrating in patches, whereas other chunks were melted to its skull like tar. Its skin was like charcoal in both colour and texture, and it was covered with massive crevasses oozing a viscous orange liquid that splattered to the floor in steaming droplets. Its stench clogged the hallway; the unmistakable reek of burning flesh and smoke.

It was fire and death.

It was a creature of nightmares incarnate—a demon of dreams.

Adelia knew it's melting skin and the smell of its burning flesh would be committed to her memory forever.

Its bottomless black eyes tried to track Ash as he danced around it, swinging his blade in a blur of white light. Adelia didn't know when he had returned, but he was desperately trying to keep the monster from moving any farther into the house.

It emitted a guttural scream and swept a massive clawed hand at Ash's head. He ducked, and as he rolled across the ground, he sliced through the back of the creature's legs, right through the Achilles' tendons. Searing lava poured onto the floor from its wounds.

Ash was all cold fury, meticulous with every movement he made, compared to the creature's fiery anger.

The creature held its hands up, and they burst into flames that jumped and danced, itching to be released. It lunged forward, grazing Ash's grey hair and singeing the ends of it with its fire-encrusted hands. They were locked in a battle of endurance and skill—the dexterous Ash with his angelic glowing blade versus the flaming shadowy humanoid who had size and strength on its side.

Adelia stood half-hidden behind the doorframe that led to the kitchen as she watched Ash battling for his life.

What in the world is that thing? And why is it at my house?

She was utterly frozen in fear. It was monstrous and was literally throwing lava across her living room floor. If it kept it up, the entire place would be engulfed in flames. As she watched from the doorframe, she noticed Ash continued to dance around the creature using only his sword. She didn't notice him using any powers, but despite that, his movements were mesmerizing to watch. He moved with a fluid grace, never missing a step or a parry against the creature's monstrous flaming hands.

"There are more coming!" he bellowed at them and shoved the creature farther into the front hall to leave room for the others to squeeze by.

"Let's go!" Novak barked. "Bring them down in whatever way you can!"

The others dashed into the front yard where three more of the frightening creatures were prowling up Adelia's drive.

Oh God, there are more? She thought in panic. There was no way they could fend off all these. They were two times the height of the Fae, three times as tall in Maewyn's case.

Despite the slower movements of the creatures, Adelia noticed they seemed to be intelligent. They knew where they were going, how to attack and defend themselves, and despite their animalistic features, they reacted like humans.

As the other three guards reached the monsters, they erupted into motion. They moved around each other like it was a choreographed dance, using a combination of blades pulled from scabbards and powers.

She watched Rory plant his feet firmly on the ground and extend his bear-like hands down toward her cobblestone driveway. He drew a shuddering breath and moved his hands towards the sky as if praising a higher power. As he did, massive chunks of stone were ripped from the ground. It was like the stone was attached to his hands with strings, and he was their puppet master. He moved his hands in an arcing pattern towards the creatures, and the chunks of asphalt followed, flying through the air like meteors of crumbling concrete. He looked like he was made of rock himself as his muscles bulged with the effort.

It was like nothing Adelia had ever seen before. These Faerie Guards seemed to be living up to their names. They defended themselves and her by proximity, with awe-inspiring intensity. The air was filled with the sounds of battle, the clash of swords, and the hissing of lava scorching the earth. The smell of smoke rose all around them, and she was grateful they lived on the outskirts of town with no neighbours close by. Adelia couldn't even imagine the look on Mrs. Schutt's face if she ambled over with her walker to see what all the fuss was about. Thankfully, she lived a ten-minute walk away down the street, or she'd probably have another heart attack from just seeing these creatures, let alone the Fae warriors battling them.

Maewyn was throwing a seemingly endless supply of daggers with terrifying accuracy. Shiny, clear daggers. Adelia realized with a jolt they were icicles, not daggers, and could just imagine how it would feel to be stabbed with ice as cold as the bars of her cage from earlier. Her icy blue eyes had turned an eerie white, as if they had frozen over in hoarfrost. The small arctic fox was darting around the creature in circles to distract it, while Maewyn focused on offensive attacks. It reminded her of a shooting star, its white fur reflecting the bright sun as it weaved between the creature's legs in dizzying figure eights.

Novak had her dual swords out, which were now ribboned with water so that when she sliced through the creatures, their skin sizzled and fizzed, steam pouring from the wounds. She kept trying to send waves towards the monsters, but they were much stronger than the force she was able to produce. They weren't even thrown off balance by the barrage of water.

The group was being pushed back closer to her house as the creatures advanced. As Adelia watched, the beast fighting Ash swiped out with its hand again, connecting with Ash's face, and sent him stumbling back into the already shattered hallway mirror. She emitted a yelp, and the creature swiveled its predatory gaze to her.

It began to move away from Ash and stalk towards her. She

hadn't been standing far enough away, so with its long legs, it reached her in a few steps.

How could she have thought standing in the doorway was a good idea? She turned to try and run back into the kitchen. She could get out the back door and shut it behind her. But the creature was too close. Before she had turned, the creature grabbed hold of her shirt. It yanked her backwards with its monstrous hands and her T-shirt collar ripped as she stumbled backward into the gigantic creature. Her back struck its chest, and instantly its fiery skin burned through her shirt, causing her skin to blister. The pain seared across her shoulder blades, her vision darkening in the periphery.

She screamed in pain and attempted to scramble away, but it had a grip on her and wasn't letting go. With every second it held on to her, the burns worsened, turning from first to second degree. She felt like she was being branded, her thoughts consumed by the burning pain, and just as she thought she was going to faint, there was a moment of slack on her T-shirt, and she pulled away frantically.

Ash had jumped on the creature's back, his blade wrapped around the creature's neck. His thick leather guard uniform was obviously magical and protected him against the blistering heat of the creature's skin. The creature dropped Adelia and was now holding on to the blade's edge, trying to pull it away from its neck. It was a battle of strength, and the monster was clearly stronger than Ash.

It ripped the sword away from Ash with terrifying force.

"What are you doing still standing there? GET OUT OF HERE!" he yelled at her as he jumped off its back nimbly. She could hear in his voice how angry he was, his eyes shooting daggers as sharp as Maewyn's icicles at her.

The creature swung back at Ash with its own sword while he was distracted, and the tip of the sword glided smoothly into the soft spot above his collarbone. His face conveyed a look of shock and disbelief.

"Ash!" she yelped, but he seemed unfazed.

"Fucker," he growled at the creature.

The creature promptly drew the sword back and attempted to charge forward to pierce him again, but Ash was ready this time, and despite the blood now gushing from his wound, he jumped out of the way. "Come on! Come at me. You may have gotten one hit in, but I will split you from nose to navel with a smile. I can promise you that." He smirked almost seductively, waiting with a twisted excitement for the creature to retaliate.

Adelia's thoughts were muddled, and it was hard to keep track of all the fighting that was raging around her, and on top of that, the stinging in her back was growing with each passing second. The situation had become more dire as she crawled away, each movement she made sending agonizing pain through her blistering back. The group needed the upper hand. She had to help somehow. She had messed up by standing around, and now Ash was hurt.

But she was a survivor. A fighter. And she'd be damned before she just continued to stand around idly.

Without a second thought, Adelia had made her decision and gingerly stood up, then hurried back to the kitchen, her adrenaline masking the pain lancing through her back. There were two sinks on the main floor: the kitchen and the bathroom. Hopefully, by the time she finished, Novak would be close enough to the house for this to work.

She stumbled into the kitchen sink and tore open the cupboards underneath and grabbed the crowbar from the pile of tools her dad kept there. Her hands were blanched and shaking, but she needed to get a grip. Adelia brought the bar backwards like she was swinging a golf club, and she connected with the old, corroding pipes under the sink. Again and again, she smashed the metal until it began to indent at the weak elbow joint. With each swing, the flesh on her back moved in an unnatural way, and she gritted her teeth against the pain.

Almost there.

She could do this. She wouldn't die here, not today. She'd survived the unthinkable before and she'd do it again.

She hit the pipe again, putting all the agonizing grief, blistering anger, and unrelenting worry she had felt the past couple hours into the swing... and finally, it burst.

Water exploded out from the pipe, drenching her clothes and soaking the floor. She blinked the spray from her eyes, then turned and ran towards the bathroom, where she did the exact same thing.

Soon more water was pouring onto the floor, adding to that from the kitchen.

She jogged through the water, careful to keep her balance as it lapped at her ankles, to the front door in time to see Novak battling with a creature right there. The creatures had gained the upper hand despite their powers, and she was now standing in the front doorway.

The creature's hands were red as the surface of the sun, and it was throwing balls of fire at her that she nimbly dodged. The fireballs connected with the brick house instead, leaving large scorch marks all over the walls.

Novak appeared to be tiring; Adelia could see her movements slowing, the sloppy way she was swinging her swords now.

"LOOK DOWN," screamed Adelia, and it took Novak a split second to realize there was water lapping at her feet.

Novak smirked, and Adelia knew she had been right to guess; Novak could only produce so much water from thin air. If the element was around her, she could use that and save energy.

Novak raised her hands, and the water began to shake. It was like she was moving the individual atoms in the water and becoming one with the element. Her eyes closed briefly, and she stilled in concentration. The water increased its quaking, like it was coming alive. Then, all the water transformed into a raging river of untamed hungry rapids, sweeping turbulently through the house, out the door, and through the gardens. The water force was strong enough to sweep the creature off its feet this time and carry it towards the cliff behind her house. The river engulfed the other three creatures, and when it reached the cliff, it plummeted down like a waterfall, and the others fell with it. They disappeared over the edge of the cliff, their frantic roaring ending abruptly moments later.

Novak bent over, hands on her knees, breathing heavily. Rory and Maewyn came into the house and helped Ash back to his feet, trying to avoid stepping on any broken glass.

When Novak looked over at Adelia, there was an unspoken thanks written across her face.

CHAPTER 8

While the group took a few minutes to regroup and take stock of injuries, Adelia snuck off to the bathroom as she could no longer endure the burning pain in her back. She realized quickly her shirt was burned into her skin in places, and she couldn't pry it off. It was agonizing. The burns were grotesque and bloody, and it was quite evident she needed a doctor.

"Damn it, damn it, damn it!" She pressed her hands to her eyes to keep the tears at bay. She may be a fighter, but she was also a crier. And today was turning out to be *too much*.

If she revealed how injured she was to the group, they would leave without her, and any hope of finding her dad went with them. She would have to cover up her injuries and hope they didn't notice.

She glanced down at the opal ring she wore on her right hand. It had been her mother's once. It was one of the only things she had to remind her of the woman she never knew. Sometimes she liked to imagine her, though. She pictured a vibrant, self-assured woman who cared deeply for the people around her. Her father never spoke of her much, the memories of her too difficult even now, so Adelia had to fill in the gaps.

The only things she knew were that her mother had died shortly after giving birth to Adelia and that her father carried a small photo of her in his wallet. Once she had walked in on him looking at it with teary eyes. He had been quick to brush them away and pull Adelia close to him, telling her that her mom would have been so proud of the girl she had become. But that was as much as he ever said about her, so Adelia found she missed the idea of a mother more. And right now, more than ever, she wished her mother were still here. She imagined her soothing voice, telling her that everything would be okay. Because it currently felt as though Adelia's world was crumbling around her. Her dad was missing, and she had just been attacked by monstrous creatures from another world. All she wanted right now was a hug.

But her mom wasn't here. She was alone. And if she wanted to avoid being an orphan and lose her dad as well, then she needed to pull it together.

Adelia wiped at the couple tears that had leaked out and steeled herself.

Harden your heart and pull forth courage, she told herself. She could do this.

Adelia then snuck to her bedroom and grabbed a worn leather jacket from her closet to put on. She winced as it came in contact with her back, white specks clouding her vision momentarily. She grabbed a pack, stuffing it full with some first aid supplies and supplies for her prosthetic as well. If she could fake this well enough, then she might be leaving for a while and needed to be prepared.

Pain was a construct and would be nothing compared to the pain of losing her dad forever. She popped a couple painkillers from the bathroom cabinet on her way back down, for good measure.

As she made her way back into the kitchen, she saw the others were patching up their cuts and scrapes with some bandages they found around the house. Ash was bandaging a burn on Rory's shoulder with practiced fingers, then he moved on to Maewyn, checking her pulse and breathing. Adelia was impressed at his efficiency and the ease with which he tended to the group's wounds. He was the last person she had expected acting as a medic. His own wound had already been bandaged thoroughly, the blood having been staunched.

Despite this, the overall feeling of the group was one of unease. She could feel it in the air with the uneasy glances and the heavy silence. They had been caught off guard and unprepared.

It had been close. Too close, and Adelia's quick thinking was likely what had saved them.

ASH APPROACHED HER CAUTIOUSLY, looking her over for signs of injury. She tried to hide the careful way she walked, to lessen his suspicion about her back.

"Are you hurt?" he asked her carefully.

"I'm fine," Adelia replied briskly.

He looked unconvinced. "I just saw you limping." He glanced down at her prosthetic leg. It was hidden mostly beneath her loose pants, he wouldn't be able to tell unless he had reason to look closer. He clearly thought it was her leg injured, not her back. And there would be two moons in the sky before she let him think she was lesser or incapable because of her leg. He was looking at her like she was a broken baby bird, pitiful and weak. But Adelia was no damn baby bird. She liked to think she was more like a falcon, easily underestimated but fierce and formidable.

"I'm just fine and dandy. As right as rain!" Adelia smiled sweetly back at him.

He crossed his arms, and Adelia hated that her gaze followed the movement or that she couldn't deny she appreciated the size of his biceps. "Fine, if you want to be a stubborn child and try and hide your injuries, then that's fine by me."

She was about to continue to argue, but then realized she should probably thank him for jumping in when he did. "Uhh… thanks for that. Back there."

She motioned with her head towards the hall that was as much a disaster as the bloody kitchen was. Ash had stepped in, all angelic with that glowing white sword of his, and distracted the creature to give her time to escape.

She hated to admit that she needed help, or that she may be in over her head. But the fact of the matter was that she still had no idea what those things were, or how they could possibly be that strong; even for a group of Fae with powers. The thought that she was even standing with 'Fae' was still absurd to her.

He smirked at her. "No problem, Goldilocks. That was quick thinking on your part. It made up for you standing in the doorway like you wanted to be dinner." He bowed his head slightly. It seemed like a mocking gesture, but his voice was sincere. She scowled back at him anyway. Calling her Goldilocks too, like he hadn't been an asshole to her for the majority of the day.

He chuckled, then looked somber again. "But seriously. Don't do that again. You almost got yourself killed, *and* you put us at risk."

"In case you forgot, I was the one who saved your asses." She couldn't help the spark of anger that flared at his tone.

"And I already gave you credit for that. But it doesn't negate your other careless choices." He stepped closer to her, his large frame obscuring her view. She had to look up to meet his challenge. Fierce falcon. She was a fierce falcon.

"Are you done?" She smiled sweetly at him, refusing to break eye contact.

"No, I'm not done. I think it's time for you to go. It's not safe here anymore, for starters. And you are out of your league. Do you have somewhere you can go?"

Oh no... no, no, no. I need to go with them.

Here he was, trying to get rid of her again despite what Novak had said about her being useful.

"Nope. I've got no one." She shrugged her shoulders nonchalantly, despite the pain from her injury, and looked down at the ground. She peered up at him through her lashes and saw he looked almost concerned. But that part was true—she didn't have any family here that could take her in. Her dad was all she had.

Then from the kitchen, Novak came striding in, clearly having overheard their conversation, and barked, "We need to get out of here. Now! Before any more come looking."

She glanced around to ensure her team were on their feet, ready to leave. Maewyn and Rory moved towards the door, but Ash held steady.

He motioned with his head towards Adelia. "She's not coming with us."

Novak's eyes were hard when she replied, "Ash, I make the calls around here. Adelia knows more about her father than anyone else, and we can't risk sticking around here to ask her more questions. She's coming with us."

Novak made it clear there were no arguments, and Adelia admired her gall. Ash was intimidating in his own right, but Novak talked to him like he was a child.

All he did was narrow his eyes but said no more. Novak then

began to make her way towards the cliff where she had sent the four creatures tumbling over.

"What were those things?" Adelia asked, following Novak's lead outside.

"Those were Molten Fae. You thought we were the only ones who would be looking for your dad? He's the one who trapped them away, and if that gate is breaking down and they are escaping, there will be more coming for him," Novak called back.

"You don't think they took him?" Adelia asked.

"I guess it's possible they already took him and sent some back to search for the key. But we don't know for sure. Your dad could have escaped and made it to Faerie."

Oh God, did Adelia hope that was true.

Novak stopped right at the edge of the cliff, a few metres down from where she had sent the Molten plummeting to the craggy rocks below. She looked fierce posed at the edge of the cliff, strands from her messy bun coming loose with the wind.

She looked back at Adelia. "It's not safe for you here. More will come. We'll find you somewhere safe to stay in Faerie. You just have to trust us."

But Adelia didn't trust them. She realized how big this all was, how dangerous this whole thing might be. However, she also knew there was no other choice for her, not really. Her dad was the only person in this world who mattered to her, and there was no way she was walking away from him.

Novak gave one last look at the group and then jumped off the cliff.

ADELIA SCREAMED and ran to the edge, peering down. All she saw was the sweeping waves below, crashing onto the sharp rocks, and gulls floating on the winds, scanning the water for their next meal. Novak was gone. It was a testament to her surprise that she didn't even consider trying to identify the gulls.

"Where did she go?" Adelia yelled.

Maewyn grinned, the white of her teeth matching her colourless hair as it blew around her in a cyclone with the ocean breeze. "There are doors to Faerie in the human world, but they aren't all easy to get to. All you have to do is jump!"

"But what if you miss? The cliff is a mile long. How can you tell where the door is?" She peered over the edge of the crumbling rock face again, this time looking for a shine or any indication that there was some hidden magical door suspended in the air above the water but saw nothing. It was a straight freefall to the unforgiving ocean.

Maewyn shrugged. "You just know." Without a second glance back, she jumped too, disappearing over the edge, followed by Rory, who glanced back at Ash for a brief second before falling.

There is no bloody way I'm jumping off this cliff.

She had always hated getting close to this cliff, and now they wanted her to jump off it? She was a birdwatcher. *A birdwatcher.* If that didn't tell them she preferred more mellow things in life, she wasn't sure what could. Standing up to Ash? Sure. She had some fire when it came to defending herself after years of ridicule, but cliff jumping? Adelia backed up, stepping away from the edge of the insurmountable drop, the ramparts of stone below more menacing than ever before. As she did, she bumped into Ash, who had been standing behind her. Her back hit his chest, and she could feel his warmth despite the cold leather—or maybe it was the heat from the burns on her back flaring up. She bit down on her tongue to avoid wincing.

He leaned down, his breath against her ear as he whispered, "Afraid?"

She shivered. She hadn't realized how much taller he was than her. When he was standing right behind her, she barely came up to his shoulders.

Reluctant to admit her fear to him of all people, she said nothing and refused to look back at him. She still felt a raging guilt at her stupidity that had nearly gotten him killed earlier.

"Hey. *Adelia*." That was the first time he had said her name. "Apparently, we need you, and I'm not going to wait here while you gather up the nerve. I don't fancy another encounter with the Molten."

"You're not much of a coddler, are you?" she noted bitterly.

He quirked an eyebrow at her. "Would it make you feel better if I was?"

"No, I assume being nice would cause you to spontaneously combust or something," she muttered.

Not that she wanted to be coddled by him. He hadn't done anything other than piss her off and underestimate her. Adelia thought back to a few hours ago when she had gotten the upper hand with him by hitting him over the head with a frying pan, tying him up, and shoving stinging nettle in his face.

It brought a satisfied smile to her face. Ash couldn't prevent her from coming, especially when Novak agreed to bring her along. He was going to have to accept that she was coming to Faerie whether he liked it or not.

But she had to figure out another way to get there... because there was still no way she was jumping off a cliff.

Just then, Ash put his gloved hands on her shoulders—thankfully above the burns—and pushed her forwards until her toes were at the very edge of the drop.

"Whoa, whoa! What are you doing?" She tried to dig her heels into dirt but couldn't get any purchase. If she resisted too much, she'd lose her balance and go over anyway.

"After you attacked me with a frying pan with no hesitation, I would have pegged you for an adrenaline junkie."

She could feel his smirk against her ear.

"You're wrong. There's a difference when it's survival instinct."

"Hmm, interesting. So you're saying all I need to do is threaten you? Maybe tell you that if you don't jump, I'll tell your dear old dad about all the very curious things I found hidden in your drawers?"

"You wouldn't," she hissed back at him, trying to spin back around so she could face him and gauge how serious he was. But Ash held her firmly at the edge of the drop.

"Oh, Goldilocks. But I would. Even just to see your face when I tell him his precious little Adelia has a naughty side."

Her face was burning. No need for the Molten to throw fire-balls at her. She'd combust from embarrassment all by herself.

She closed her eyes and tried to steady herself, but the fear of jumping off was crippling. Her terror mounted with each ragged breath and her legs felt weak. Her chest tightened, numbness taking over.

This jump, this precipice she was standing on, stood for so much more than just a doorway to Faerie. If she jumped, it meant she was vaulting into an unknown world, with unknown people. Away from the only home she had ever known. Her comfort, the familiarity of Bark Beach—all gone.

No.

She shook her head, ready to admit she couldn't do it, but then his gloved hand grabbed hers, interlocking their fingers.

"What are you doing?" She tried to rip her hand away from his.

"I'm holding your hand, obviously."

"And *why* are you holding my hand?" She wasn't about to admit it actually felt soothing. That it maybe calmed her nerves.

"I'm being sweet and reassuring."

"Bullshit. You're not the sweet and reassuring type either."

She looked up at him standing beside her, his grey hair wild in the wind, the sharp points of his ears barely visible. His light caramel eyes glinted mischievously in the sunlight.

Ash shrugged in defeat. "You're right. I'm not."

But instead of letting go, he tugged. And Ash pulled her off the cliff with him.

CHAPTER 9

She was falling.

Speeding toward the earth like a peregrine falcon mid-dive, except this was nothing like flying. She was hurtling downward, everything around her a blur. She had no control, like she was hydroplaning across a flooded highway after a torrential downpour. The only thing tethering her, keeping her from losing all sense, were the strong fingers clasped around hers. She could feel Ash's hand still holding hers, and she gripped it forcefully, fearing what would happen if the wind broke them apart.

Then suddenly, she was standing on the ground, as if it had been a dream. Ash had already dropped her hand and had started to walk away after his friends.

"How *dare* you pull me off that cliff against my will?" She jogged to catch up with him.

Ash didn't even deign to look back at her as he said, "I didn't have the patience to wait for you to stop acting like a scared little girl."

"I'm pretty sure not wanting to jump off a cliff is a fairly reasonable thing to be apprehensive about." She was yelling now.

He stopped and whirled around to face her. "So far, all you've shown me is that you freeze when things get intense and you're afraid to take risks."

"Are you kidding me? I literally knocked you unconscious when I found you in my room!"

His eyes darkened. "That was just lucky. You'll need to do a lot more than that to prove me wrong."

Adelia threw her head back. "You're infuriating."

"Right back at you." And he turned to stalk away again.

Still fuming, Adelia took in her new surroundings, and her breath hitched in surprise. How did she not notice where they were as soon as she landed? Around her were hundreds of colourful houses, all painted in shades of blue, from cerulean to cobalt, with worn thatched roofs. There were birds perched on every roof, everything from eagles to small songbirds.

And they were all singing.

It was a symphony of bird songs and calls, so bright and lively that the notes seemed to be coming alive on the wind. The notes wove together in a blissful melody, wrapping around her heart and speaking to her in a way only nature could. Most were shocked to learn Adelia could identify every bird in her area by song alone. One time while riding the bus, a boy had come over to sit beside her and flirtatiously asked what she was listening to. She removed her earbud and passed it to him, mainly to see his reaction.

She could hear Roger Tory Peterson's voice saying, *And now we move onto warblers, what many refer to as the gems of North American birdlife,* followed by the sweet song of the yellow warbler. His face had been priceless. Needless to say, he hadn't asked for her number.

She strained her ears now to try and identify any of the birds around her, excitement building.

Birds were flying around in a meticulous pattern, a sort of dance where each one knew precisely where the others were and where they were going. It resulted in a kaleidoscope of colours that blurred across the sky.

Adelia stood there, awestruck. *This is the most beautiful thing I've ever seen.*

The streets were bustling with Fae, all moving with the same fluid grace as the ones she came here with. She watched, mesmerized, as two beautiful Fae men walked down the street laughing, with their wives trailing behind them demurely.

It was a place out of a storybook, and Adelia understood the look of disgust Novak gave back in her bedroom when she was talking about Teilio moving away from Faerie—her house in Bark Beach was nothing compared to this.

Her amazement was abruptly extinguished as she realized how much more amazing this would have been with her father here. Not only to share in this discovery of her heritage, but to have someone understand the excitement and awe she was feeling. To have her dad smile quietly as she twirled around, absorbing the birds zooming around, trying to identify each one before it flew away.

He would have pointed out birds that crossed their path, asked questions, and listened intently while she provided endless details from species to native habitat. He would have truly enjoyed it, beaming with pride at his daughter and watching her experience a world beyond imagination.

Her sorrow at his absence took her breath away. A bittersweet taste filled her mouth at the thought of finding a place that spoke to her soul, a place where she felt like maybe she could genuinely belong one day, and yet not be able to share it with the person she cared about the most.

I will find him. Whatever I do, I will stand here with him and relive this moment with him by my side. He always told me life's moments mean more when you share them with those you love.

Adelia steeled herself and closed her heart again. As much as she wanted to find him, she knew she couldn't do it alone. These people—these Fae—were her only hope.

She could lie and deceive them if they could reunite her with her father. They may be friendly right now, but Adelia still barely knew them.

Her thoughts then drifted to Ash. He seemed so opposed to her coming along, like they didn't need any help, but he had been the one to stay behind. Yes, he had pulled her off the cliff, which she still wasn't too happy about, but he could have left her there. It was a perfect opportunity to ditch her like he wanted. That moment of compassion was at odds with his fierce determination to be rid of her. She took a steadying breath, her pulse lowering with each intake of air, and moved to follow the guards.

SHE CAUGHT up with the rest, as they veered off the main road and began weaving down small alleys. Burrowing owls scampered around the garbage like raccoons, darting in and out, twisting their heads in full circles to watch the group pass by.

"Where are we?" Adelia asked Maewyn, who was trailing slightly behind the group after trying to pet a burrowing owl with no success.

"Welcome to the Wind Court." She smiled at Adelia in return. "I'm a little biased and think the Snow Court is more beautiful, but this place has its redeeming qualities." She said it in a sarcastic way that implied she knew how beautiful it was here too.

"This is the main city, Zephyr." She gestured around her to

the quaint homes and exquisite gardens filled with floating hummingbirds and vibrant butterflies. "There are other smaller towns that are considered part of the Wind Court, but this is where most of the Wind Fae live."

Adelia couldn't peel her eyes away from the flurry of activity around her. The city was as alive as the wildlife it teemed with.

"It's absolutely breathtaking here."

Maewyn shrugged. "This part of the city definitely is. But there was a war here, remember? Many areas are still being rebuilt. Some might never be."

"Why not?" Adelia asked.

"King Orodani of the Wind Court focused his efforts on certain areas and left some... uhh, less affluent... areas to fend for themselves." She seemed rightly ashamed to convey this fact.

"Oh. That's horrible. Is the King well-liked?"

Maewyn shook her head. "Yes! He's a great King. Well, from what I've seen of him, at least. As far as I know, he doesn't leave the castle much, and he lets the princes do a lot of the work for him." She shrugged again. "Obviously, they felt their attention was needed in other areas of the court."

It seemed odd to Adelia. That a well-loved King could stay well-loved despite leaving his citizens to suffer. The same King who apparently was angry at her father for using the key improperly, even though it saved hundreds of Fae. It didn't make sense.

"Is every court a monarchy?"

"The Wind Court is ruled by King Orodani and his three sons. One of them went missing a few years back—went off on his own, I guess—and the other two help run the court. The other courts are also ruled by kings, except for the Molten Court."

"Who rules the Molten Court?"

"Queen Karai." Maewyn shivered, then the fox at her feet

copied her motion and shook as well. It seemed as though Maewyn didn't want to say anything else about her.

They followed Ash, who weaved through the maze of alleys with the confidence of someone who could do it with his eyes closed. He was chatting softly with Rory.

"Where are we even going?"

"To your uncle Tadriel's house! Ash grew up here, in the Wind Court. He knows his way around and where all the people are who don't want to be found. Tadriel was also a soldier in the army at the time your dad was. He helped a lot with the creation of the key. He also went into hiding after the war but didn't leave Faerie altogether like your dad."

Her uncle Tad was also a soldier? The picture she had in her head of him didn't match. Not with his unruly hair, spectacles, and lanky body.

"My uncle lives here? I can't believe I never knew *any* of this."

Maewyn smiled. "Yes, and I'm sure you have lots to ask him as well."

Adelia decided to continue asking questions while she had Maewyn's attention. "So tell me more about you guys. The Faerie Guards, I mean."

She took in the black fighting leathers and long gold-trimmed cloak Maewyn wore. It was so dark, it made her skin look pearlescent. Maewyn didn't wear weapons like the others, but after that battle earlier, she knew Maewyn was deadly in her own right.

"Oh, sure. Well, you can think of us as elite warriors. We are dispatched to different courts to deal with issues that arise. It can be anything from civil unrest, apprehending criminals, or controlling any beasts that invade cities from nearby forests or mountains. So, I guess, in a sense, we are peacekeepers too. Our headquarters are located in central Faerie for that reason." She seemed to be growing in excitement as she talked. "The little symbol in our cloaks identifies us as Faerie Guards. We even take an oath before joining."

She took a deep breath and recited, *"For Faerie we will protect and serve. May magic give us strength, be our blade with which we fight. May we always bear faith and allegiance to our fellow guard, for their strength is our strength, their power our power. Only together are we whole."*

After seeing them all fight back at the house, it made sense; they moved around each other with practiced ease and they were stronger as a team. The oath made it sound like they were a family, that they shared in all their experiences, and Adelia's nerves were eased slightly at thinking of them all like that.

Maewyn continued with her explanation as they meandered through the streets. "You should see how beautiful it is at headquarters! At the centre of the headquarters is the Orb. It's where all the power from your world gets converted to magic here."

"The power from my world?"

"Yeah! The magic here doesn't actually come from the elements, even though it might look like that. We get our magic from the earth and natural disasters that occur in the human world. Those natural disasters produce energy, and all that energy is harnessed and converted to magic here. So, you have the Terrain Court; they get their magic from earthquakes and landslides. The Wind Court feeds off of tornadoes and hurricanes, stuff like that. The Aqua Court gets power from tsunamis and flooding, and then I'm a division of the Aqua Court. The Snow Court. We feed off blizzards and avalanches. There are divisions of some courts like Storm Fae, a division of the Wind Court, but they are incredibly rare. Only a few left in all of Faerie. They harness power from lighting storms. And lastly is the Molten Court; they get their power from volcanoes and forest fires. Those are the ones we encountered back at your house."

Adelia reeled at the knowledge. Yes, natural disasters were incredibly powerful, but in the human world, they were feared. The few times a hurricane had hit the coast in Bark Beach, it was absolute carnage.

Maewyn continued, "In your world, when it's hurricane season, for example, the Wind Court grows in power. You can feel it; it's like drinking an energy drink. The power will radiate through the air, making a Wind Fae stronger than before for a short while. There has been a lot of volcanic activity lately in the human world, giving the Molten a chance to grow more powerful."

Adelia shuddered at the excited way in which Maewyn spoke about this. It really showed her the difference between these Fae and humans. How could they embrace and enjoy something like natural disasters? Something that resulted in the deaths of so many humans. Then she realized with a jolt, she was one of these Fae. She probably had a power that she could draw from the very same energy source.

She vowed that even if she were to learn magic, she'd never take joy in where it came from.

"All the energy is then concentrated within the Orb and converted to magic power here in Faerie. It floats all around us." She held her hand out like she was catching an invisible snowflake.

"This is all so wild. And what about this fox of yours? Is it a pet?"

"A pet!" Maewyn screeched loudly. She looked offended and bent down to pick up the small fox that had been walking at her side. "His name is Rin. He's my familiar. Think of him like a piece of my soul. We are connected in ways that no pet could ever be. Many Fae have them, but not everyone. Finding a familiar is equivalent to finding a soulmate—something everyone longs for and wishes for, but not everyone is so lucky to experience."

Adelia looked down at the fox, and his gaze reminded her of the small Cerulean Warbler she had encountered at the banding centre. She tried to be nonchalant as she asked, "Are everyone's familiars foxes? Or do some people have birds, for example?" She gazed up in time to see a macaw flapping past, its stately scarlet feathers a bold streak of colour against the midday sky.

"Oh no, it really depends on what court you are from. Most Wind Fae have birds or bats, where the Aqua have sea creatures. The Terrain have mammals, and Molten tend to have reptiles as familiars."

That little bird then... was it someone's familiar? Did her dad have a familiar still despite being in the human world? Maybe someone had sent the warbler with a key; it certainly would explain the bird's unnatural strength and intelligent eyes. Adelia hoped that meant she was supposed to have the key, that it had been delivered to her for a reason.

The streets grew narrower and narrower as they walked, with more litter and garbage floating along the now empty streets. The paint on the houses was less vibrant, chipped and peeling. They were more of a faded grey-blue and looked like they were long overdue for maintenance. She noticed graffiti decorating the walls of some homes. Most was an eyesore, but they passed a large flower painted on the side of one building that was shaped like a trumpet. They were clearly on the outskirts of Zephyr.

They finally reached a faded white door set into a long building that blended in as well as a grouse in a field of freshly fallen snow. The average Fae would walk past and never notice it. It looked as if it was a back-alley door to a restaurant or shop out front. Ash was the first to approach the door and knock quietly.

They heard some shuffling from the inside, muffled by the thick walls, followed by the door opening a crack. Her uncle Tad stood there, hair wild, ink staining his dark brown face. He looked completely unhinged. Alarm flared in his eyes to see four Faerie Guards outside his door, who made no attempt to appear harmless.

"No! Please! I swear I didn't do anything!" He took a frantic step backwards. Then he noticed Adelia standing among them and his eyes widened with disbelief. She gave him a tentative smile and waggled her fingers at him in hello.

"Adelia?" He stepped back to the door and abruptly shut it in their faces. You could hear the unlatching of multiple locks, and then it swung open to reveal him in rumpled pants and a stained tunic. "What in the Orb are you doing here?"

"Hey, Uncle, um... these are my friends. Can we come in for a bit?" She cringed internally at calling them her friends. She barely knew them and was lying to them at this very moment, making them go on a wild goose chase for something she already had with her—no time to dwell on that, though.

Bewildered, her uncle showed them into the small house, clearing some space at the table that was covered in old books with cracked spines. She could see the books were filled with scribbled words and drawings of mysterious objects in the margins. The house was as rumpled as he was. It was dark and dusty, and moldy plates of food were scattered about the tables and chairs. It smelled stagnant. Adelia assumed he spent most of his time cooped up in here hiding, which would be incredibly difficult considering how beautiful it was *out there*. He appeared weary and weathered—years older than the fifty she knew him to be.

It was hard to imagine the Wind King was that unforgiving.

That her uncle feared for his life so intensely that he had condemned himself to a life of solitude in his cramped little home. Hadn't her dad and him stopped the war? Maybe things went wrong, but didn't they still accomplish what they were supposed to? The King should have treated them as heroes, not criminals.

Tad's eyes darted back and forth between the guards now in his living room. Ash had his arms crossed, leaning back against the counter with a bored expression.

"So, I assume you're here about Teilio," Tad stated gruffly. He ran a hand through his hair absentmindedly. "I'm sorry I couldn't do anything to stop him. He was only here for a few hours, then he went to the gate. I guess he thought it would be good to inspect the magic seal. See how long he actually had to fix it before the gate broke completely... I'm not sure. But I haven't heard from him since."

Adelia jumped up. "He was here? He's okay?" Hope flickered again.

"He was injured. But I fixed him up and then he left. I tried to convince him not to go."

"How long ago was—"

Novak held her hand up to block Adelia. "We just need to know if he had the key or not."

Adelia balled her hands and bit her tongue from lashing out at Novak. How could Novak not understand that she cared about finding her dad? She understood that the group only wanted the key, but they couldn't expect Adelia to do the same. It only made her affirm that she made the right choice in not telling them about it. Novak would surely kick her to the curb if she found out about the key.

Tadriel shook his head. "He wouldn't tell me. I sent him with my familiar Cerla, and she came back without him this morning."

"Your familiar?" Adelia asked.

Tad nodded and whistled a sharp, insect-like tune. A little Cerulean Warbler came fluttering out from the bedroom and landed on his shoulder. It seemed to remember Adelia from their encounter earlier. Its eyes lingered on hers longer than the others.

She was glad these familiars couldn't talk because it surely would have blown everything.

But this information meant it was her dad who had sent the key to her?

But why?

It wasn't adding up.

Tad sighed. "Why don't you all have a seat and I'll tell you more."

Novak took the armchair, while Maewyn and Ash claimed the couch. Rory paused in front of the couch and crossed his arms. "You two are seriously going to make me sit in the middle?"

Maewyn giggled but merely patted the middle cushion. With a huff, Rory squeezed into the middle of them, looking like a mammoth on a Barbie couch. Adelia sat on the floor in front of the couch. In this position, she was able to curl her knees to her chest and hug them tightly. It was oddly comforting, like she was holding herself together—both physically and emotionally. Rin, the arctic fox, nestled beside her, just below Maewyn's feet. Adelia rested a hand on the fox, to which it began purring. His fur was like a cloud, and she had an overwhelming urge to scoop him up and nestle him in close.

"Adelia, are you going to tell me how in the world you got here yet?" Tad pushed his spectacles farther up his nose and shifted uncomfortably in his chair. He was a wiry man, always fidgeting and moving whether he was sitting or standing. He and her father had been best friends for as long as she could remember. He'd come for a weekend and stay with them in Bark Beach and it had always been a treat. It would be a weekend filled with sunny outdoor barbecues and Uncle Tad sneaking Adelia sips of his drink when Teilio had turned around. She trusted him almost as much as her dad. But when it came to explaining what had transpired today, she wasn't even sure where to start.

"Molten attacked her house, Tadriel," Ash replied gravely.

Her uncle snapped his weary eyes to her, looking for injuries like Ash had done back at the house. "And you got away?"

Ash nodded. "She's lucky we were there when it happened. Four of them. Fully changed."

"Excuse me, but how do you two know each other again?" Adelia interjected.

"Ash worked at a well-known shop in Zephyr for a while. I frequent it often," Tadriel replied. He raked a weathered hand through his dark hair. "So, Teilio. I'm guessing he never returned home, Adelia?"

Adelia shook her head. "No. I came home from work to the kitchen soaked in blood and these four in my house looking for him as well. Actually, now that I think about it, why did you have blood on your clothes, Ash?" She looked at him accusingly.

He raised a brow at her. "We ran into some nasty trolls on the way to the door to the human world." He glanced down at his still blood-stained cloak. "Needless to say, it didn't fare well for them."

"Okay, enough of that," Novak cut in. "Did Teilio have the key with him when he was here? That's what we're looking for."

Tadriel shook his head. "Of course not. I have no idea what he did with it. Threw it into the ocean? Buried it ten feet underground? Whatever happened to that key is a mystery, and only he knows the answer. At the time, I thought good riddance. We didn't want it ending up in the hands of the wrong Fae."

Novak closed her eyes briefly and took a steadying breath. She looked at the group around her, looking each of them in the eyes, and finally at Adelia. "So Teilio is the only one in this entire world who knows where the key is, which means if he went to the gate and never came back, then I guess we are going to the Molten Court too."

CHAPTER 10

Tad decided to let them stay with him for the time being. The space was cramped, but there was enough food for them all to eat their fill.

A powdering of dusk was filtering in through the frosted windows, and the group decided to take the rest of the night off. Tad cleared spots for everyone to curl up for the night either on the couch or floor, and there were enough blankets to go around. It certainly wasn't her bed at home, but she wasn't going to be the first to complain. Adelia just imagined she was camping. The floor here wasn't much different than a hard forest floor.

Before tucking into bed for the night, they all sat around the living room, relaxing—Novak lying on the couch she claimed as hers, Maewyn lying on the floor playing with Rin, and Rory and Ash chatting. When she was sure no one would notice, Adelia crept out of the room, her feet light on the hardwood floor. The pain in her back pulsed angrily as she slid into the kitchen to find her uncle. She needed to show him her injuries and get some help.

He sucked in a breath when she pulled off the leather jacket she had been wearing to reveal the red skin and scorched shirt still stuck to her back.

His voice was hoarse when he spoke. "Oh, by the Orb, Adelia. This is really bad. We need to get you to a healer right away."

"No!" she interjected quickly. "I can't. I need to stay here. Please, I'm begging you. I need to help them. I can't sit by and do nothing. It's my *dad*. He needs me." The words felt choked coming out. Heat prickled behind her eyes, and she blinked rapidly to try and stop any tears.

He looked at her with such profound pity, it made her sick. "Oh, Adelia. He would never expect you to put yourself at risk like this for him. Look at yourself! He would have my head if he knew you were here, and I wasn't taking care of you."

"Then help me take care of this burn. You should know me by now. I might not be a Faerie Guard, but I'm not useless."

He sighed, running an exasperated hand through his hair again. "I never said you were useless."

"Then don't try and stop me, Uncle."

Silence followed, and Adelia thought he might not reply.

"Okay. *Okay*, if you trust these friends of yours, then I won't argue. They better protect you as if you were one of them."

She didn't bother to tell him that they had made no such promise. That she had only met them that day. Or that if they knew she held the key they needed, she had no idea what they would do to her to get it.

TAD SPENT the next hour meticulously removing the burned bits of shirt from Adelia's back while she bit down on the sleeve of her jacket to try to silence her hisses of pain. He lathered the burns in a healing salve and bandaged her back. He told her it would heal faster than usual—magic healing ingredients tended to speed up the process—but for her to still be careful for the next couple of days.

"Why didn't you tell me?" she asked him in a small voice after he had finished.

She wanted to know why they had kept her away from this world, segregated to the human realm. Never learning about her true heritage.

"Oh, Adelia. I wanted to. I really did. But your dad thought it was best to keep you hidden from this place. After everything we went through, he was afraid. He was afraid his actions would have consequences for you, that he'd be punished for disobeying orders and using the key early. He couldn't risk it. Not when you were so young, and it was just him."

Adelia nodded, listening intently, and he continued, "He used a spell. One to hide your features. It seems to have worn off now that you're back in Faerie, but you were so young when he took you to the human realm, you didn't recall anything of life here. I know it might be hard to understand, but he did it for you."

"Wait—it's worn off?" She lifted her hands to cup her ears and try to feel them. "How is that even possible? I didn't even feel anything!" She had always liked her ears. She wasn't sure how she felt about them changing.

Tadriel nodded. "You should go look in the bathroom mirror. I really am terribly sorry, Adelia. We never meant to hurt you."

She tried to understand—she really did.

But it still felt like a betrayal.

WHEN SHE FINALLY HAD A FEW moments to herself, she stood in front of the bathroom mirror, staring at her reflection. Her hair was a tangled mess, and she could see the tiredness in her eyes. The last day had felt like a hurricane rolling in, and she was a little songbird trying to stay aloft as she flew through it. She'd had so little time to reflect on the situation she was in now, where she was, and what they were doing.

What would Ron do when she didn't show up to work tomorrow? Would she ever find her dad? Go back to normal life? It seemed doubtful. She didn't even look like the same person anymore. She reached up in disbelief to poke at the pointy ears that had appeared.

The spell *was* broken.

It was all the confirmation she needed that this wasn't a dream.

The girl looking back at her in the mirror was more elegant and polished than she has ever looked in her life. Other than the ears, there were no major changes. It was more of a *vibe*. She looked healthy. She looked like a brighter version of the old Adelia. Which was completely disconcerting. Did this mean she could never go home? Did she even want to go home anymore?

It was like she was a different person, but she felt the same as always. She had tried to put on a persona of this fearless, stubborn girl before Ash and the guards, but the truth was that she was terrified. Every time she closed her eyes, even for a moment, she saw her bloody kitchen floor or the monstrous Molten Fae with their melting faces. The images were burned into her retinas, surfacing whenever the world stilled. It was a reminder to her that the world was anything but calm. Calm was something the old Adelia relished, but now? Now, calm meant she was being idle, not taking action. Calm could mean the end of her father's life.

She had to keep pushing the guards to do more, to act faster.

The clock on the wall mocked her with its persistent ticking.

Tick. Another second wasted.

Tick. He might be already dead.

Tick.

Tick.

Tick.

She was running out of time.

SHE HAD to sleep on her side that night. Her injuries were too sensitive and sore to attempt lying on her back like usual. Before going to bed, she had made sure to wash her stump with the antiseptic soap she'd packed and let it completely dry out. She'd hobbled back to her makeshift bed, everyone else already asleep, and set her leg beside her gently. Wearing her leg to bed was asking for sores. One small blackhead or pimple could turn into a raging boil if she left it on too long. But cleaning her leg and her stump every night was just a part of routine now. It wasn't a hassle, it was life. A life she would be grateful to still have each and every single day. It was weird. She normally wasn't shy about telling people about her leg—when she didn't forget about at least—because frankly sometimes she forgot her leg was a prosthetic. But the guards made her nervous to divulge that part of herself. Had they ever met anyone with a prosthetic before? Would it change their perception of her? Would they think her less, or weak? For now, she'd make sure to wake up before them to put it back on.

It was a fitful sleep. Every time she closed her eyes, visions paraded behind her eyes. Dreams of the Molten Fae and their burning flesh. Their withered hands reached out for her. Ash getting stabbed in the shoulder over and over again.

She finally gave up, weary-eyed and restless. She went to the kitchen to make some tea and ease her shaking hands. Everyone else was fast asleep, and peaceful snores from Rory rumbled quietly through the house.

She held the steaming cup in her hands and didn't even notice Ash joining her at the table until he spoke, startling her slightly.

"Can't sleep either?" He cocked his head to the side, flicking his hair out of his eyes like she had seen him do back at the house.

Adelia shook her head. "It's been a bit of a day for me, in case you forgot," she snapped.

He shrugged indifferently. "No one expects you to be the hero of this story, Adelia."

"What's that supposed to mean?"

"You want to save your dad. We can all see that."

She had come to the kitchen for some peace and quiet. Not to fight with Ash, but she couldn't help herself. No one had pushed her buttons like this in a long time. "You don't think I'm capable?" This. This is exactly what she had been afraid of. They already doubted her.

"I never said that. I meant you don't have to pressure yourself to become something you aren't."

"You don't know me."

It was a fair point, though. She had always figured her life's story would be filled with baked goods, birdwatching, and beach days. She had thought one day she'd get married and buy a house down the street from her dad. She had never planned on *this*, but now she had to decide if she wanted to go back to her old life. She wasn't so sure anymore. Being in the court for the first time was magical. It felt like a dream and she could see how happy she'd be living in a world like this. Especially if they saved her dad.

She might be afraid right now, but did that have to be a bad thing? Fear was a cage, and she felt compelled to break free. She wanted to find out how strong she actually was—in both body and mind. She wanted to be someone people could rely on. She wanted to be strong for her dad.

She looked up at him with hard eyes. "You don't know me at all actually. You don't know what I'm capable of."

He stood up to make his way back to his cot. "Please, by all means, prove me wrong."

Furious. She was furious.

Who was he to say what she was capable of? He was purposely trying to instill doubt in her, to convince her not to come with them.

Why was he so opposed to her coming along? The thought plagued her well into the night, chasing away any hopes of returning to sleep. She sat on the kitchen stool until her tea was cold, and the sun was streaming in the small window above the sink. Finally, she rose and took the time to put on her liner, gently rolling it up her limb to ensure no air was trapped underneath. Then came the sock and prosthetic, followed by the sleeve to keep it securely in place. She tested her weight, deciding it felt secure and comfortable for the long day that was surely ahead. Only then she finally heard rustling from the other room and knew the others were waking.

ONCE EVERYONE WAS UP and moving, Novak decided to start on their plan of action. Her cobalt hair pulled back into a tight braid today that seemed to mean business.

"All right team. We have to divide and conquer. We need to stock up on equipment and food. Make sure our weapons are polished and sharpened. Anyone who still has healing injuries needs to tend to them. It will be harder to keep them clean and sterilized once we are in the forest. Lastly, we need a blueprint for what we know of the Molten Court."

"Only a few things," Rory muttered sarcastically.

Novak smiled at him. "You can come with me, Rory, to get as much done as possible then." It was as if she knew he'd rather stay here and relish in the last few days of comfort before leaving.

"Only if we stop and get air cakes for the trip," he countered.

"What are air cakes?" Adelia asked.

"Only the lightest, fluffiest, most decadent dessert you've ever tasted in your life."

She could see his mouth watering at the thought.

Novak rolled her eyes, but a smile played at her lips.

"Fine. You can be in charge of the food. I'll stock up on everything else. Maewyn, Ash, you stay here to work on the blueprint. After we are organized, we leave for the Molten Court. Adelia, you will stay here with your uncle."

Which meant Adelia had very little time to figure out a plan to convince them to let her come along.

Novak left with Rory to pick up the supplies, leaving Ash and Maewyn to start with the blueprint.

Adelia sat patiently, watching them draw out a blueprint of the Molten Court; entrances, guards, and possible places Teilio could be if he had been taken hostage. It was panning out exactly how Adelia had initially wanted—they had pinpointed where her dad had gone, and they were planning a rescue mission. But after seeing the Molten Fae who had attacked the house earlier, it did nothing to ease her nerves. They were gruesome and incredibly powerful. Them kidnapping her father was not something she wanted to think about.

"Why did the Molten Fae look like monsters if you all look normal?"

Ash kept his head down, ignoring her question, but Maewyn looked up to answer her.

"The Molten War was mainly a conflict between the Wind Court and the Molten Court. The Wind King had discovered that Queen Karai of the Molten had been tampering with forbidden magic. It's a big no-no here. Forbidden magic is powerful and unpredictable and it has permanent effects on the user. Many of the users transformed into lava creatures, husks of their original beings. They became stronger and almost unstoppable, but it changed them. Fae who use forbidden magic lose their sense of self. Basically, once you start using it, it's almost impossible to stop. It's like a drug. So, the Molten you saw yesterday were once normal Fae, but they are barely recognizable now. If your dad hadn't stopped them during the war by forging the key and imbuing it with magic to stop them from invading the Wind Court, they would have destroyed Faerie."

Despite the morbid talk of forbidden magic, Adelia felt a surge of pride knowing her dad played a role in saving Faerie. That was the man she knew, not some dangerous soldier in an army, but someone who was actually trying to save people. She thought about how nice this was too; to be chatting here with Maewyn. She exuded radiant energy, always smiling and welcoming. Despite her colourless appearance, she had a colourful personality that shone through in everything she did.

"So, what is forbidden magic exactly?" she asked.

"Forbidden magic is using non-natural magic by draining the power from others around you. It's a quick, easy fix to becoming strong, and for the Molten, probably what they thought was a sure way of gaining power. But you can't do it without harming the person you steal the magic from. It's like draining them of their life force." She shuddered.

"You've never tried it then? You are all so powerful."

Maewyn looked affronted. "Definitely not. It's taboo. Only criminals and the Molten have ever dared to use it. Normally, as guards, one of the things we do is track down and apprehend anyone who has dared to practice it. But that's enough about forbidden magic. I hate talking about it. Why don't we talk about your powers?" She squeaked excitedly. "Don't you want to try using them?"

Adelia realized she hadn't given it much thought. She had been so preoccupied that she completely forgot about the fact that she might actually have powers.

"Oh. Right. Do you think I will be able to harness any power?" Adelia asked.

Maewyn giggled. "Of course! You should get Ash to show you." She looked across the room at him. "He doesn't use his own wind power. He likes to stick to his swords." She lowered her voice to a whisper, "And don't ask why, he's never told us, but he'd be a great teacher regardless." She looked thoughtful for a few minutes. "He really is a good guy. He's just independent and can come off as cold because of it."

"I don't know if I'd say cold. Aggravating, yes. Acting like he's some higher power and we're all bugs beneath him? Most definitely."

Maewyn looked guilty at that. "Give him a shot. I think you two would actually get along."

Adelia nodded and glanced over at Ash, head bent over a book, his pale hair falling across his eyes again. He hadn't seemed to hear what Maewyn had said, but with his pointed Fae ears, she wondered if he was faking it.

Maewyn stood up. "I'm going to go out into the market. I have a few things I need to pick up." She looked from Adelia to Ash, her eyes brightening, and gave Adelia an encouraging nod. Then she closed the door behind her, leaving Adelia and Ash alone.

CHAPTER 11

ASH

Of course Ash could hear them talking about him. It's not like he was sitting far away. Which meant Maewyn was doing it on purpose.

She constantly attempted to guilt him into doing *good* things. Like that time she had detoured their mission to help an elderly Fae man move. It turned out he was a hoarder and it set them back an entire day in their travels to the Blacklore forest to deal with a swamp golem there. And of course she had volunteered Ash to catch the man's *twelve* cats and move them. His arms had been peppered in scratches and his mood had been deplorable by the end of the day. But the old man's smile had rivalled Maewyn's, and Ash's cold heart had melted just a bit. Not that he'd ever admit that to anyone.

And here she was, trying to get him to do it again. They had no reason to teach Adelia how to use her powers—other than to be nice. And he didn't do nice with random human girls. With random anyone for that matter. Even if he couldn't stop thinking about the fact that she had *actually* tied him up with scarves on her bedroom floor. Or what it would be like if the roles were reversed. For him to be standing over her, teasing her until she was begging. If her moans would come out all adorable and breathy. What it would be like to slip—

Ash shook his head vehemently. He needed to stop now. Adelia hated him, which was for the best. He didn't even know the girl. She was basically a human and—by the Orb, he needed to stop stealing glances at her.

He couldn't start thinking that being around Adelia was fun or enjoyable. He wasn't ready for anyone to get close to him like that again. He had Novak, Maewyn, and Rory. They were his family and he didn't need anyone else.

"What do you think, Rin?" He bent down to pet the artic fox that had plopped down beside him. "Should I help Adelia learn how to use her powers out of the goodness of my heart?"

Rin's dark button eyes bore into his. And of course he didn't answer. No one but Maewyn could tell what the fox was thinking. Not that she could communicate telepathically with Rin—it was more like they just always knew what the other was thinking.

Ash bent down to scoop Rin off the ground. But Rin wasn't a pet, and he didn't appreciate being treated as one. He nipped at Ash's fingers, drawing blood, and Ash abruptly dropped him back down on the ground.

"Little fucker," he muttered while cradling his hand. "This is what I get for trying to be nice."

Rin trotted back over to Maewyn's side, his backside turned to Ash as if to say *You're going to have to try harder if you want my affection. I don't cuddle up with just anyone.*

Damn it—even the fox wanted him to be a better person.

"I know I'm going to regret this," Ash muttered to himself again.

Even though he knew he would be a great teacher.

He was great at everything.

Maybe he'd make Adelia beg and grovel a little. That'd be amusing at least.

He glanced up subtlety to watch Adelia scowl at Maewyn before the white-haired girl gave him a knowing smile and walked out the door with Rin in her arms.

CHAPTER 12

Whether to ask Ash for help was a toss-up. Maewyn had left already and Adelia found herself bubbling over with anticipation on how to learn magic. But Ash was already an arrogant asshole and she feared asking him would result in a barrage of snide comments about his superiority. But he was a Wind Fae like her. It made sense to learn from him.

"Will you teach me how to use my powers?" Adelia asked, hating herself for how desperate the question came out.

She waited.

"No."

And that was it. This truly solidified how much of a jerk he was.

He hadn't even bothered to look up from his notes.

Adelia stood and briskly strode around the stained little table towards him. She leaned over and shut the book in front of him with a dusty thud.

"Everyone else is off running errands, while you are sitting on your ass in this dank room, pretending to read so you don't have to talk with me. You can spare a few minutes. Helping me out is not the end of the world." Adelia really didn't want to plead. He wasn't worth it. If he was going to be a jerk and refuse again, then she could find someone else.

He rolled his caramel eyes before locking them with hers. "Maybe if you ask nicely, I will. I think you forgot to say please."

Adelia bit her tongue. "*Please* help me with my powers," she ground out.

He feigned thoughtfulness for a moment, placing his long fingers beneath his chin in deliberation. "Hmmm. I think I'd be a bit more inclined if you begged a bit more. You could even get down on your knees for me. I'd never say no to that." His smirk was vile.

"Hell no!" Adelia sprang upwards, her face burning hot. "I am *never* going to do that."

"Come on now. Don't say never." He stood. "But that's okay. Making you all flustered is enough reward for me."

He made his way to the front door, paused, and looked back at her. "Are you coming or not?"

Oh, how badly she wanted to smack that arrogance off his face with a frying pan again.

BEING BACK OUTSIDE in the fresh air was as surreal as before—the wind was breezing through the blossoming trees, sending loose leaves dancing across the sky. A king vulture floated on the thermals high above, reaching dizzying heights. Adelia watched it above her as she walked, tripping only a couple times, which was frankly pretty good considering she never watched her feet.

She glanced over at Ash, who was watching her. "Have you never seen a bird before...?" he asked, amused.

Clearly, her gaping mouth and awestruck reaction to the

birds were abnormal for the Fae living here. She hesitated. "Well, I'm what people call a birdwatcher. You know, I search for birds, keep track of what I see. I use these," she said sheepishly and held up her binoculars for him to see. Then she glanced back down, confused at why she had decided to tell him.

He was silent for a few seconds, then burst out laughing. A pure, sparkling laugh that, in any other circumstance, Adelia would have loved to hear. He had been so cold, barely smiling since she had met him other than the odd cruel smirk.

However, to have him laughing *at* her, laughing at her one true passion, that was not the type of laughter that made her smile. She felt a burning shame course through her. She was Adelia, the weird girl who liked watching birds, a hobby nobody understood here either. She didn't even try to hide the hurt on her face. What was she thinking? Why would she tell him? He hadn't shown her that she was anything other than an annoyance to him so far.

She began to walk away, tired of having to explain herself and her love of birds to people. Tears pricked the back of her eyes again. Damn her watery eyes.

Ash reacted quickly and caught her by the arm before she got too far. His gloved fingers curled around her slender arms, squeezing gently. "Whoa, whoa, sorry I laughed. I was just caught off guard. There's really no point in birdwatching, as you call it, in Faerie. You don't have to go searching for anything here. Every bird you could imagine is right here in the court." He glanced at her as if trying to read the emotions hidden beneath her eyes.

"Come on. I want to show you something."

ASH LED her down the main cobblestone pathways in silence.

His demeanor had changed slightly, like he was more aware of her. She noticed out of the corner of her eye that he kept glancing at her as they walked. As if to make sure she was still with him and hadn't tried to walk away again. She noticed his gaze fell to her leg again, but he remained silent.

They meandered through the city, closer and closer to a spiraling tower that reached up to the sky, touching the clouds, far above any of the other smaller homes around it. They entered through the heavy, intricate metal doors that banged shut behind them. Adelia found herself standing in a small room with no doors other than the one they entered through. A man was dozing in the corner, head lolled back, mouth agape, in a blue and silver coat. It had the silhouette of a birch perched on a wire embroidered into the top left corner by his heart.

Ash cleared his throat, and the man startled awake. "Ahem, sorry, sir. Ma'am." He nodded to Adelia. "Going up?" he asked.

Ash grinned in his mischievous way, the half-smirk Adelia was growing accustomed to, and he reached out to grab her hand. He laced his hands through hers, and she could feel the rough leather of his gloves against her palms. He gave her hand a squeeze that made her heart jump.

"Does this mean we are going to do something crazy again?" she asked hesitantly.

He pretended to look affronted. "Me? Do something wild and crazy? Never."

He gave her a wink, then looked back at the young man waiting, and said, "Whenever you're ready."

A gust of wind started at their feet within seconds, shooting upwards with enough force to lift her feet off the ground. Adelia realized with a jolt that the 'doorway' was above them. There was no ceiling, just a giant hole in the small room that looked like it reached up to the top of the spire miles above them.

The wind picked up, and they shot through the sky; up and

up until Adelia couldn't see the ground below. It was like riding an elevator without the enclosure. It felt like her stomach had been left on the floor as they rose higher and higher, the walls of the spire speeding past in blurs of colour.

Ash was still holding her hand, but she was losing her ability to stay upright. She was practically horizontal now as the wind carried them higher.

Then the wind shifted to the left, and she crashed to the floor in a belly flop. Ash landed gracefully on two feet and dropped her hand.

"What was that?" she growled. She gingerly stood, dusting the grime off her pants from landing on the floor. Her hair was absolutely wild, and it would take her hours to brush through the tangles after the cliff jumping *and* invisible elevator ride. Her heart was still hammering, adrenaline coursing through her veins so aggressively that her legs felt shaky despite being on solid ground.

Ash was still smiling, his caramel eyes glittering with amusement as Adelia watched him.

"I know you probably can't get enough of my gorgeous eyes, but you should really look around you, Goldilocks. I seem to be quite the distraction for you."

Blushing, she quickly looked away and around as he told her. The blurs of colour she had noticed on the trip up were actually birds. The whole spire was filled with perches for them. The room was shaped like an octagon, with every other wall open to the elements for the birds to fly in. The rest of the walls were filled with roosts and nests. The ceiling was latticework where a multitude of birds had made more homes. All around her were squabbling jays and chirping sparrows, falcons dozing, and ducks curled up with their heads tucked into their wings. Herons stood perched, preening themselves while a group of bee-eaters took turns diving off their perches to catch bugs that flittered past.

"It's The Perch. For all the Wind Court's familiars," he said, interrupting her thoughts of amazement. "Where all the birds around come to rest. I thought you might like it. Maybe one of these birds will become your familiar one day too."

There were hundreds—no, thousands of species here. More than Adelia thought she would see in her lifetime.

"How am I supposed to add all these to my list," she wondered out loud.

Ash chuckled. "Well, maybe one day we can come back with a notebook and pencil. We'll start one bird at a time." He seemed different; he appeared more relaxed than before. The stiff way he held his shoulders had relaxed slightly, his thumbs looped in his belt. Swallows dipped and dived around his head as he leaned casually against a pillar in the room.

"Why did you bring me here, Ash?"

He shrugged. "When I saw how you looked at all the birds outside, I figured you might like it here." He started to walk in a lap around the room, looking at all the slumbering familiars. "I always liked coming here when I was growing up. It may not seem like it would be peaceful, with all the squawking and singing, but I thought it was. Helped drown out all the other things rattling around in my head."

"So you're telling me you decided to do something nice for me *just because*?"

He looked at her seriously, but she could see the laughter behind his eyes. "Don't get used to it. I was feeling particularly generous today."

"Wow, lucky me."

"So, what do you say we give this magic thing a go?" he asked.

Adelia brightened, both nervousness and excitement

duelling within her. Maybe it was her imagination, but up here, she was floating. The energy of the familiars surrounded her, and it made her feel like she could fly herself.

"Picture the magic in the air like a smoke-filled room—it's everywhere, and if you take a deep breath, you can inhale it in. The smoke permeates your skin, your clothes, and it seeps into every nook and cranny. Magic is all around us; it's in the air. You just have to feel it."

She cocked an eyebrow at him. He made it sound so simple. She took a minute to imagine what he was talking about, to try and feel the magic around her, as if it were tangible.

She felt nothing.

She looked at him dubiously.

He held his hands up in defense, still smirking at her. "Ok, fine, fine, we'll try something else then." There was something about how he smiled; it made her forget why she was here in Faerie, searching for her missing dad. Or the fact that she was lying to him about the key. His smile was so genuine, his expression unguarded. He actually looked happy for the first time since she had met him, happy to be here with her, and it was infectious. She couldn't place the feeling she was having, why the reckless grin on her face hadn't gone away since landing up here.

"Close your eyes," he said as he stepped closer.

She did.

She sensed him standing right in front of her, and he smelled like rich earth and campfire smoke. It was comforting and reminded her of home. She had an urge to close the distance between them, as he continued unaware.

"Now I want you to think about how it feels standing at your house, on your cliff, right before a storm. The wind howling, deafening in your ears. How it would feel to then bottle that storm. To collect all the wind in a jar, until it's still and unmoving around you. And then, imagine what would happen if you opened the jar again and you let the storm come rushing back out all at once."

She tried to focus on his words, letting them permeate and soak into her subconscious.

"I want you to imagine that you are the jar, and you hold the power of wind inside you. Let it all go. The wind bottled up inside you, causing a storm in your heart, let it out and into the world."

She obliged. She imagined that she could stop time. She could steal all the wind from the world, the trees would pause mid-gust, and flags would fall in its absence. She imagined a storm was building up inside her. All the pain and rage she had felt over the last day mixed with it and became a storm inside her blood.

She was a hurricane.

She was a force of nature, and she could harness the power of the wind.

A wisp of wind left her fingers, and her eyes bolted open in time to see an invisible force knock Ash backward. He stumbled and caught himself just before plummeting down the hole in the floor.

He looked backward, only inches from the drop, and said sarcastically, "Well, clearly, I thought this location out quite well." He smoothed his cloak back out. "Good job, Goldilocks. You made enough wind to make a grown Fae stumble. I'd say it's pretty good for your first time."

Adelia beamed. She was actually really proud of herself, but then she thought of the boy below who had effortlessly risen them both up forty stories without a second thought. She thought about how powerful the Wind King must be and what he could do. She wondered what her dad could do if he was one of the most powerful Fae in the Wind King's army. She was learning so much about this world and more and more about what her dad's life had looked like before her. It made her wonder how much he missed it.

Right now, she felt more alive than she had had before. It was electrifying, her pulse was thrumming, and the hair was standing up on her arms. All she wanted to do was continue practicing. Bring the storm inside her alive again, to improve. It felt like she had lightning in her veins, rippling through her.

She glanced back at Ash as he scanned the room and all the birds lining the walls. The few that had been sleeping beside Ash when she created the gust of wind looked thoroughly displeased, their feathers ruffled after hours of preening.

"Thank you," she said sincerely. "I mean it. This means more to me than you could ever imagine. Being here... it's one of the most amazing things I've ever seen. And thank you for teaching me how to get started."

He slowly closed the distance between them and she had to crane her neck to look at him. His eyes were shadowed, his breathing a little heavier. Probably just from the adrenaline of almost being knocked off the perch.

He reached out to tug on a curl that had fallen over her eyes. "Does this mean you forgive me for laughing at you?" He smirked and she couldn't help but smile back.

"It's a start."

"Good, I wouldn't want you to hit me over the head with a random household object again." His hand lingered near her face, his gaze dropping to her lips for such a short instant, she was sure she'd imagined it.

He pulled his hand away from her face, but she found herself hoping he wouldn't. There was something about him she couldn't put her finger on. Why did she want to be close to him? Why did she feel drawn to someone like him?

She wanted to reach forward and grab his hand again. But

this time, she'd peel his gloves off. She wanted to feel the skin of his hands, always hidden away. Would they feel like fire when he touched her, amplifying the warmth crawling up her neck and flushing her cheeks right at this moment? The adrenaline of using her powers for the first time, the joy of being in this tower with all these familiars, and being this close to him were overwhelming.

"Ash, why don't you have a familiar?" she asked him.

As soon as the words came out of her mouth, she regretted them. She could see the visible change in his demeanor, as he seemed to pull away from her and retract back inside his cold shell. She could feel the shift in the air between them, the breaking of the spell.

Despite him being so close to her, she could feel him closing his walls to her once again. The mask of arrogance snapped on, indifference clouded his features, and the glimmer in his eyes faded away.

"I'm sorry. I didn't mean... You don't have to tell me," Adelia rambled, trying to pull him back to her, to stop him from closing up on her entirely again.

"My familiar was taken from me a long time ago," he said coolly.

It was too late. He wasn't going to open up; it was clear he didn't want to talk about it. Adelia wondered what tragedy must have occurred for him to feel like this. She remembered Maewyn saying that Rin was a part of her soul and realized it must have felt like Ash lost a part of himself. She wondered if it was like losing her father, someone so important to her that she would do anything to have him back.

He stepped away from her, looking back down the wind elevator. He signaled down to the ground, and she felt a fluttering as the wind began to pick up from below.

CHAPTER 13

Ash and Adelia found themselves back at Tadriel's house, the group reconvening after a busy afternoon of errands. Maewyn scurried over to Adelia as she walked in the door beside a brooding Ash.

She thrust a bundle of clothes into Adelia's arms and squealed, "I got you Wind Court clothes! So you don't stand out so much."

Adelia looked down at her blood-stained khakis, her crumpled shirt, and mud-caked hiking boots. She had completely forgotten how disastrous she appeared.

Maewyn continued, "Don't worry, they are practical clothes! Although it was very tempting to buy you one of the Wind Court gowns. They're made to look like birds themselves, all wispy and flowing." She twirled around as if she were in a gown herself, but her cloak twisted awkwardly around her legs instead, and she laughed. Adelia found it was hard not to smile as Maewyn beamed up at her.

"Maewyn, you really shouldn't have." She tried to interject, but Maewyn promptly shushed her.

"Hush now. No take-backs."

"But—" Adelia tried again.

Rory came over to join them and rested a bear-like hand on Adelia's shoulder. "You've been through a lot in the last few days, Adelia. Take them." His tone held a finality that she didn't bother arguing with.

Adelia conceded and Maewyn proceeded to rush her towards the bathroom.

She felt a stab of guilt as she tried on the clothes. They were a thick material and had clearly cost Maewyn money, whatever kind of money they used here. Adelia didn't deserve this kindness from Maewyn. Soon they would be heading to the Molten Court to get the Molten Key. The key Adelia had in her pocket. She was putting Maewyn's life on the line because of a lie; she was risking everyone's lives. Based on how they spoke about the Molten Court, this was not going to be a walk in the park. It would be dangerous. She had no idea if the team would still agree to help her if they knew she had the key, but she couldn't imagine they would. They had only met Adelia a few days ago, and they owed her nothing.

She pulled out the little key in her pocket and held it in her hands. It still felt hot in her palms, but it seemed heavier now than before. Like the weight of her guilt was tied to it.

Her guilt settled into her stomach like a bad meal. How was it possible to be both right and wrong in her decision? She had always thought she was a good person, but every time she saw the key, it reminded her that she may not be.

She was a liar.

A deceiver.

Someone willing to risk the lives of those around her, for her own gain, and that thought made her feel sick. Adelia shook her head. Maewyn and the others had been so good to her thus far. They could have thrown her out at any moment. They could have found her another place to stay in the Wind Court, but it seemed like they actually enjoyed her company. And Adelia was beginning to enjoy theirs as well.

Maewyn was a bright ray of light that exuded so much energy, it was intoxicating. Novak had a constant, steady confidence and faith in her team and everyone looked to her for guidance. Ash was a puzzle she was just learning to solve. There was so much more to him than Adelia had initially thought. Yes, he was arrogant and standoffish most of the time, but he also showed her that he could be kind. And then there was Rory, who Adelia had barely spoken to, but she found herself hoping she would get the chance to know him better as well.

She had been so distrustful of them at first, but after just a few days, they were slowly breaking down the walls she had put up. She thought it would be easy to lie to them, to use them to get what she wanted, but she found herself caring about what happened to them now. If something happened to any of them during this mission, she would feel responsible.

But she had come too far—despite all these new feelings, she couldn't abandon her dad. She toyed with the thought of telling them, hoping they would save her dad anyway, but she wasn't so sure.

And it wasn't worth the risk.

Her dad's life wasn't worth the risk.

A FEW MOMENTS LATER, she emerged from the bathroom in her new outfit. She decided to string the key off the gold necklace she always wore. It was a gift for her sixteenth birthday and the only jewelry she wore other than her mother's opal ring. The key settled onto her skin, hidden from view between her breasts, reminding her why she was here and what she needed to do. The heat from it against her skin ignited a fire in her veins. She would continue to do whatever she needed to get him back.

Maewyn squealed yet again as she emerged in her new Wind Court outfit. It consisted of tight dark brown pants that hugged her hips in all the right places, with matching leather boots. The shirt was a loose long sleeve that was breathable and featherlight. It was an earthy sage that brought out the green in her hazel eyes. It appeared as if the shirt was floating around her, like she was standing in the wind elevator again. It came with a leather bodice that wrapped around her, providing a protective barrier around her vital organs. Matching leather arm bracers covered her forearms and tied together with thick straps. All the leather was detailed with a delicate gold pattern that looked like veins of a river branching out.

It made her feel powerful, like a hero in a book. She looked at the team gathered around the table—the team going into the Molten Court soon. She still barely knew them, yet somehow was beginning to trust them.

"I want to come with you," she stated to the team. "I know I can't fight like you. I know my powers aren't as developed as yours, but I think I can be an asset."

She knew it was a weak argument. She had run through the scenario in her head repetitively and practiced how she would make her case, but it hadn't come out even close to how she wanted. She *needed* to go with them. This was her chance to find her dad, and she wasn't staying behind while they went without her.

Novak appraised her new outfit and grinned. "I'm glad you want to come. I've changed my mind. The new plan we came up with, it hitches all on you."

"Wait. What? It does?"

She couldn't believe Novak had conceded. She really thought she would have to argue or worst case sneak along.

Novak leaned back in her chair and crossed her arms. "Yes. It does. Do you think if we waited a few days to leave, you could master your powers better?"

"Yes! I can!" She would do whatever she needed. And she certainly wasn't going to question Novak's decision to bring her along.

"Ok. Start working harder then. Any spare time, I want you to practice."

Adelia nodded. It was settled then. They were all going to save her dad.

CHAPTER 14

The next day, the team was working on the last pieces of their plan to infiltrate the Molten Court when Tadriel entered the room. He held out a small translucent vile filled with a similarly clear liquid for them to see. He gestured for them to gather around him, Adelia's shoulder brushing against Ash in the cramped space.

He began, "I'll explain this in detail for Adelia's sake since I assume the rest of you know this." He gave Adelia a pointed look and continued.

"All objects can be imbued with magic. For example, a powerful Aqua Fae can imbue the water around them with magic. This is important because, at the time of the war, a small group of us worked on defence measures against the Molten. Your dad"—he looked at Adelia again—"was the one working on the key. He imbued the key with powerful magic and created a permanent magical barrier around the Molten Court. However, as we mentioned before, he was forced to use the key before it was completely ready. I wasn't there at the time of the event, so I never knew exactly what happened, but over the last couple days, while you were all planning, I tracked down an Aqua that was there at the time. Another soldier working in the lab."

Adelia wasn't really following where he was going with this information yet, but she kept listening.

"And I found out some fascinating information. After he was forced to use the key, before he fled, Teilio had an Aqua Fae take and make a duplicate of this from him." He held up the small bottle. Its contents seemed to glimmer in the sunlight filtering in through the window.

"It's a memory. You have fluid in your brain and spinal canal that a talented Fae can extract, and that fluid can hold an abundance of information. This one here is from right after your dad used the key. Maybe it will help you understand how the key works."

"Tadriel, you are brilliant!" exclaimed Maewyn.

Without further ado, Tadriel uncorked the bottle, and the water inside seemed to come alive. It acted as though it was in space, flowing upwards out of the bottle and into the air around them. The small room's air became hazy as a scene unfurled in front of them, suspended in the water.

Adelia felt her father's thoughts flood her own, like she was inside his head, living the memory herself.

THEY HAD GOTTEN *through the city walls, tearing apart the quiet, unsuspecting homes of the Wind Fae as they raged down the streets to the looming castle of the King at the heart of the Wind Court.*

Teilio looked out the window and saw the fires spreading across the thatched roofs, the smoke, thick and suffocating, billowing into the air. The hoard of Molten, who no longer even looked like Fae, surging towards his exact location. They were grey and ashy, with cracks spreading across their skin that seeped viscous orange lava onto the streets, leaving sizzling puddles. Their eyes unseeing, red with rage—

the eyes of what used to be good men and women before forbidden magic.

Seeing this, Teilio knew he didn't have time to gather the council. He'd originally intended for the most powerful Wind Fae to use the key together—a drop of their power to seal the gate would be like taking a cup of water from the ocean.

There was only one option, and Teilio knew he had no choice.

It was this or it was over.

In the moments before the Molten broke down the main gate, he began to pour every drop of his own power into the key. It started as a wisp flowing down his arms to the tips of his fingers, leaving them numb and shaking. He steeled himself and pushed harder, and the wisp became a gust as he felt the force of his magic that was tied to his soul being sucked out.

It was a vacuum, taking everything that he had to give, pulling with the force of a black hole, and it was attempting to make him yield everything to it.

He knew then that he wouldn't have enough power. The key would keep taking from him until there was nothing left of him.

He wouldn't survive it.

Teilio closed his eyes and thought of his daughter, four months old, still doe-eyed and cooing in her crib.

He couldn't leave her.

She would have no one.

This key, this war, would not take that from him. It could take all of his magic, a part of himself he didn't even realize was possible to live without until now, but it couldn't take him from her.

If he could do it, stopping now would leave the Molten key with less magic than it needed to properly seal the gate. It would trap Queen Karai and the remaining army inside the Molten Court, but any Molten here in the Wind Court would not be transported back to their own court. He hoped the King's army would be able to defeat this first wave of soldiers, especially knowing no backup would come. It was the best he could do, and Teilio felt no remorse for that. He had given his life to the King over and over again already. He would not let this life he had chosen for himself, a life of war and destruction, devastate his family.

Adelia *was more important than all of this.*

All he had to do was let go.

But he felt like he was falling, completely unable to catch his breath with the wind whipping past him. Teilio screamed as he felt the last of his power being ripped from his soul, and he forced himself to drop the key from his hands at the last second.

It went clattering to the ground and skittering across the laboratory floor.

Teilio fell down, empty, a husk of what he was before. He was a sky without colour, air without wind. He felt as though he had taken a breath in, but it was no longer filled with oxygen. The emptiness was like a void he would never crawl back out of. He would never be the same again.

A Fae without power was no longer a Fae.

Teilio was no more than a man.

THE PICTURE and thoughts that were swirling around them began to fade. They all stood there quietly until the water was pulled back into the bottle, and Tadriel sealed it again.

Novak was the first to speak. "This means even if we retrieve this key, we can't use it. We aren't strong enough." Her voice was shaking slightly as she spoke. "Damn it!"

She slammed her fist against the desk, sending pencils and papers flying into the air. Adelia flinched at her sudden outburst.

Maewyn went over to her and placed a hand on her back. She spoke in a soft voice, like trying to calm a wild animal. "It's okay. You'll get another chance to prove yourself. We didn't even know if this was going to be possible. It was an insane assignment to begin with. And maybe they'll still promote you even if we get the key. We all still think you're amazing, Novak." You could hear the sincerity in her voice, and she tried to put her arms around Novak in a tight hug. Novak pushed her off and walked away without saying a word. The door slammed shut behind her and the room felt heavy.

Rory broke the silence first by clapping Ash on the shoulder gruffly. "Looks like she's taking after you, Ash. You're the one who normally has temper tantrums."

Ash gave Rory a withering look, one that could wilt the most vibrant of flowers.

Maewyn looked conflicted. "Should I go after her?"

Rory nodded. "Probably. She has a soft spot for you. Just try and force her into another hug and maybe she'll reciprocate if we aren't standing around watching. We all know how tough she is, but she still thinks she has to put on a façade, even in front of us." He shook his head, some of his hair coming loose from its bun. Rory reminded Adelia a bit of Aquaman sometimes—his hair was *so* lush. She never thought she'd be so jealous of a man's hair. But was she ever.

"Why was she so upset?" Adelia asked the group.

Maewyn buttoned up her cloak and she and Rin left the house as Ash replied, "We were supposed to use the key when we found it. To reforge the gate. But with only four of us... it looks like it will be too powerful. If they were originally going to get the council to use it, our powers come nowhere close to theirs."

"What about me, though? I can help."

Ash chuckled darkly. "No offense, but your power is so limited right now, if you gave up any of it to the key, you'd be human again. Just like your dad."

Okay, fine. She had just found out about these powers. She wasn't ready to give them up yet, as selfish as that was.

"We'll have to play it by ear. Find the key first. Then figure out what's next," Rory said reasonably.

THE NEXT FEW days were a whirlwind of collecting necessary supplies, polishing weapons, and securing travel means. Ash hadn't offered to take Adelia out again to practice, so Rory had accompanied her to teach her how to use magic instead. He was the strong, silent type, offering instruction when needed, but otherwise letting Adelia slowly master the wind.

She was improving infinitesimal amounts each day, creating more wind than the little gust she had produced the first time while working with Ash. Each time she opened her senses to the magic around her, it was like her blood started thrumming with electricity. She had discovered other tricks she could do, like using the wind under her feet to be soundless while she walked or lift and carry small objects to her on a gale.

All of it was surreal. Adelia never imagined that her love for birds would be ever more than just a hobby. But she now knew that it was a part of her. Her love for the outdoors, the sky, the wind, and the creatures that called it home were all tied to her heritage.

Each time she took to the streets with Rory, to head to the small meadow just outside the city centre to practice, she would gaze up at the birds zooming past. The birds here had become the colour of her dreams, and whenever she needed to be reminded of the joy and beauty of life, they were there. She would watch the starling's murmurations and listen for their soft wing beats. It was music for the ears and eyes.

Today, she closed her eyes, knowing it would be their last

day in the Wind Court before leaving. She opened them again to find Rory watching her.

"Tell me, Rory, why is Novak really letting me come with you guys? She could have easily found a more powerful Wind Fae to bring with you."

It was the one thing that had been bothering her since Novak had agreed to let her come with them. Yes, she was improving, but she was still no fighter. It was odd that Novak had involved her in their plan so readily, all previous reservations forgotten. Ash certainly had voiced his displeasure at letting her come along.

Rory looked thoughtful for a moment, his strong features softening. "Each Faerie Guard team has five members—we used to have another. His name was Daxon, Dax for short. He was a Wind Fae like you. He was never a particularly good guard... but he was like family. He was pretty wild too. He certainly liked his whiskey, and would use each successful mission we had as an excuse for us all to go out and get a drink. You can probably guess Ash never approved of the relaxation and revelry, but it was good for him too."

Adelia noted that Rory spoke about this Dax in the past tense.

"A year ago, we found out that Dax was a Molten sympathizer. He had begun to spin these preposterous tales that the Wind King—*his* King—was the one behind the war. That the Molten Queen was never at fault and had attacked the Wind Court as retaliation."

He shook his head; it was true sorrow that shone in his eyes.

"He tried to convince us. But he obviously had no proof. Just his wild ideas that the King was corrupt and he had to stop him. He made his way to the Molten Court. We had known at that point the gate was weakening. He was convinced he would camp outside and petition for entry to the Molten Court when it got weak enough. I'm not sure what set him on the path or how he convinced himself that entering the Molten Court wouldn't end in certain death—especially as a Wind Fae. But we never saw him again."

Adelia was speechless. She hadn't seen much of the Molten Fae, minus the attack at her house, but she couldn't imagine them being friendly towards anyone.

Rory continued, "I think Novak has been nervous about trusting anyone since then. But then we met you. You are invested in this for your own reasons. We all know you want to save your dad. But I think, if anything, you are more determined than all of us put together to succeed in this."

Adelia absent-mindedly brought her hand to her chest and felt the key sitting at the hollow of her throat. Rory's eyes tracked her movements, and though she knew he wasn't able to see under her cloak, she hastily dropped her hand.

"You're right. I'm going to give this mission everything I have."

Rory nodded. "We know. Trust is important to Novak. And we trust that you'll give it your all."

Rory was right. She would give it her all. But that didn't mean they should trust her—not completely. She was lying about the key, after all.

But then Rory nodded to her. "You know that we all know, right?" He said it softly, like he was almost afraid to broach the topic.

Her heart sputtered to a halt. They knew? They knew about the key? And they hadn't tried to take it from her?

"You... you know?" She couldn't get anything more coherent out.

Rory smiled softly. "We're guards. Our job is to be observant. I don't know if you didn't bring it up because you didn't want us to judge you, or doubt you, but none of us would ever do that. I just thought you should know that before we leave. So you don't have to keep hiding it."

Wait a second.

How he was phrasing this wasn't making sense.

"Uhh... what are you talking about?"

"Your leg, Adelia," Rory replied. "You know, Faerie is a dangerous world. It's common for someone to lose an arm or a leg, or sometimes even just born without. Their elemental limbs look a little different than yours, but it's the same concept."

Her leg. He was talking about her leg. She wasn't sure whether to be relieved or not. She had been hiding it from them, or so she thought, for days now. She had convinced herself they wouldn't let her come on the mission, that they *would* judge her. She'd let her insecurities take over. She looked down at her leg shamefully. Her leg was a part of who she was and she'd forgotten that. And she didn't need to be ashamed. She was a survivor, a fighter, and her prosthetic leg was only proof of that.

"We call it as prosthetic at home," she whispered, glancing up to finally meet his gaze.

"Can I look at it?" he asked tentatively. She nodded and Rory came up and crouched down.

She pulled her pant leg up to her knee so he could see the full thing.

The look of amazement on his strong features made her heart squeeze.

"This is unbelievable. What's it made of?" he asked.

"It's mainly titanium. A strong but lightweight metal."

He stood back up, dusting off his pants. "Fae make their prosthetics, as you call them, from their powers. They tend to blend in that way, but yours is badass. You're badass, Adelia." He smiled at her, and she couldn't help but grin back. Yes, she was an amputee. Yes, she lived with a disability, but she wasn't alone.

Even here in Faerie apparently. Before coming here, she was a huge advocate for disability acceptance and greater awareness, and here she was forgetting everything she preached about. Dealing with a sense of embarrassment was something she had struggled with when it first happened, a desire to pretend like nothing had changed. But she was a different person than she used to be. She had gone through so much shit and she was so much stronger because of it. It was that strength she'd use to find her dad.

"Ok, time to practice more. Let's see you try and lift my shield off the ground." He placed it flat on the grass, took a step back, and Adelia practiced.

AFTER HOURS OF GRUELING TRAINING, Adelia was absolutely winded. She chuckled at the pun.

"You're getting significantly better. I think you'll be ready," Rory announced gruffly. The mid-day sun of the Wind Court was beating down mercilessly. Adelia was sweating, light-headed from lack of water. Rory, on the other hand, despite his dark hair and bulky size, looked as comfortable as a rhino in the desert. His thick skin was glowing in the sun.

Adelia sat down on the ground gracelessly and sprawled out on her back. Rory approached and sat down beside her, handing her a skin of water that she graciously gulped down. She rolled her head over to look at him. "Tell me, Rory, why did you decide to join the Faerie Guard?"

"Being as tall and bulky as I am, it seems to me it was an easy decision," he replied blandly.

Adelia rolled onto her side and propped her head up with her elbow.

"Come on. Other than the obvious."

"Fine. In the Terrain Court joining the Faerie Guard is

viewed as an honour. Not many Fae are selected and thus being chosen to protect our world is viewed as brave. But on top of that, did you know that you get a stipend for being a guard?"

Adelia shook her head.

"We get paid a generous amount. But our families do as well. That was actually the main reason for me joining."

That was unexpected.

"You do it for the money?"

Rory smiled sadly. "I do it for my family. I have seven younger siblings and it's just my mom at home. It absolutely broke my heart to leave them—to leave her—but being here gives them a life they would have never been able to have regardless. I work for the Guard and can sleep every night, knowing they are safe, with a roof over their heads, and food in their bellies. Without the stipend that's sent to them, they likely would have been in the streets by now. And as much as I miss them, I know leaving was the right choice."

"Do a lot of Fae join the guard for the money then?"

Rory shook his head. "Surprisingly no. It's a hard life being a Faerie Guard. We are basically nomadic, travelling across Faerie, never settling down roots anywhere. It's also a dangerous job."

"When was the last time you saw them? Your family I mean."

"About a year ago. We passed through the Terrain Court on a mission and I was able to visit, but I haven't since then. After we finish all this craziness with the key, I'd like to go back. See how much the little ones grew in the last year."

Adelia smiled. "I'd love to have a big family like that. You're very lucky to have so many who care about you."

And she did. She had always wished for a brother or sister that would join her in making sandcastles on the beach, or playing make-believe in the backyard. She loved her dad dearly, but she had to wonder if maybe having a sibling to socialize with would have made her less awkward when it came time to make friends at school. That was something she had always struggled with.

"I'm guessing you don't have any siblings?"

"Nope. Just me and my dad... I know it's only been a few days—and compared to the year you've been without your family that's nothing—but I miss him a lot."

"We'll get him back, Adelia. I know it's not good he was taken by the Molten, but it was lucky that he has the key. So we can all work together to get what we want."

Why does he have to be so damn nice? Adelia thought belatedly.

Rory pushed himself up off the ground with the grunt and held out a hand for Adelia. She grabbed it and he hoisted her up effortlessly.

"You've had enough for today. Let's head back."

"Thank goodness. I was worried you were going to say let's keep going."

"I can tell when I've pushed someone a little too hard. And when you start letting my rocks hit you because you can't hold your wind shield anymore, it's time."

"Fair statement," she replied, rubbing at the small bruises that would undoubtedly appear on her arms from that. She wasn't quite sure if she completely believed she was ready, but she didn't have a choice.

CHAPTER 15

After her conversation with Rory, Adelia found herself losing her resolve to keep the key a secret. Every time she walked into a room with the others, she almost told them about the key. Keeping it a secret was weighing on her, but every time she opened her mouth to confess, it was as if she could hear her dad calling out to her.

She could hear his plea for help, echoing in the back of her mind, and she would mumble some lame excuse for what she had been about to say instead.

Once they rescued her dad, she planned to ask him to lie about having the key with him. He could give them the key and they would never learn that she had been wearing it all along.

Tonight, they would leave for the Molten Court and from what she had been told, it would be as close to Hell as she would ever get. It wasn't just because it was filled with the blood-thirsty Molten, but because of the perilous molten lava river and steaming geysers that littered the territory—or so she'd been told. She imagined it was going to be like walking into the seventh circle of Hell.

Maewyn joined Adelia at the little kitchen table where she had been packing her bag. Well, her uncle's bag that she was borrowing. She hadn't brought much of anything with her. "Are you feeling nervous about leaving tonight, Adelia?"

"*Ha*, just a bit." She kept her head down as she filled the pack with rations.

"It's ok. I think we all are. This mission will likely be one of the most dangerous we've ever been on." She paused, looking guilty. "Actually, I probably shouldn't have told you that. That would definitely just make you more nervous." She grimaced.

"Who decides what your missions are?"

"Our commander at the Orb does, Ardrok Goldsleeve. He assigns groups to different tasks and we were assigned to this one. Novak has been trying to get promoted at the Orb for a long time, so she jumped at the opportunity for a big mission like this."

"I'm not surprised. Novak seems like the type of person who wants to move up in the world."

"Well, she's spent her entire life dedicated to the Faerie Guard. Being recognized for her hard work is all she's ever wanted. She grew up in the Orb, you know." Maewyn grabbed her own pack, a steely blue one, and began to pack as well.

"What do you mean she grew up there?" Adelia asked.

"She's what they call a child of the guard. She was orphaned during the war, and subsequently taken in by the guards. It's where a lot of orphans end up. Raised to be soldiers since they no longer have any family."

"I had no idea..." It struck Adelia as shocking because Novak had always seemed so composed. She would have never guessed. Novak must have gone through so much as a young girl amid the war. Adelia shuddered to think of the bloodshed she must have witnessed.

"Novak has worked so hard, but Commander Ardrok has

glanced over her at every promotion. She's desperate to prove herself."

It made Adelia look at her in a slightly different light whenever Novak barked orders to her team. She lost her family, which should have left any young girl fractured and broken, but she had found purpose here, with these people, with the Faerie Guard. Adelia could only admire her strength because she had been so close to breaking down when she discovered her father was missing. And she still had a chance to save him, unlike Novak with her family. She couldn't imagine the life she would have lived if her father had died that day he first used the key. She could have been an orphan too. She would have grown up here in Zephyr. Would she have become cold and hardened like Novak? Would she have still found a passion in birds? Or would she have been motivated to become a Guard like her father and follow in his footsteps?

Since learning the source of the key's power, Novak had become more aloof. She threw herself into tackling the details of the plan. She spent countless hours searching books on the history of the Molten Court to complete the blueprint of the castle to the best of their ability. She assumed they would have to break in. Since Teilio had never made it back, they believed he was there.

Adelia and Maewyn finished packing their bags and moved to find the others.

Ash had barely spoken to her, or anyone else in the group, since he had taken her to The Perch. He was preoccupied with his own thoughts, and if Adelia didn't know any better, she would have said he seemed scared.

He paled whenever they spoke about Queen Karai, and the haunted look in his eyes became more evident with every detail snapping into place. She wondered if he lost his familiar in the Molten War, and if the thought of going into enemy territory was triggering, but he definitely wouldn't tell her even if she asked.

That much was clear.

He had opened up to her, only to shut back down again. It was like he was afraid to let people in, to let anyone get close to him.

Which made her want to do it even more.

THEY FOUND the others sitting in the living room, watching Rin chase a mouse around.

Wait.

A mouse!

Adelia shuddered. Yes, the house was a disaster, but mice? She cringed at the thought of there being critters running around while they had been staying here. When they got back, Uncle Tad would have to be ready for Adelia to help him with some major spring cleaning.

Novak motioned her to come sit. "All right, Adelia, to get to the Molten Court, we have to travel through the Blacklore Woods."

She pulled out a map from her pocket and sprawled it out on the floor. She pointed to a large, green splotch on the map in front of them. It extended outwards from Zephyr and ended before what appeared to be an extensive mountain range. On the other side of the mountains lay the Molten Court.

"Okay...?"

Novak continued. "It's a stretch of dense forest that weaves throughout Faerie and delineates each of the courts. I'm sure Maewyn told you that as Faerie Guards we protect the lands from various threats, one of those being creatures from the forest." Novak gave her a severe look. "The forest is perilous, but still less dangerous than going through the treacherous mountain pass around it. Both are filled with dangerous creatures, lethal plants, and poisoned waters."

"Sounds *just* lovely." Of course, Faerie couldn't be all colourful birds and quaint thatched homes. This was precisely what she *had* expected before she got here.

Novak continued, "The fastest way to the Molten Court is through the Starlight Caverns."

"Those don't sound so bad." She brightened at the name.

"Well, they are. You have to promise to stay with us. As long as we're together, we'll be safe."

Adelia nodded. She wasn't foolish enough to run off in an unknown Faerie forest alone, especially one filled with dangerous monsters.

"Say it," Novak demanded.

"I promise."

Novak nodded, satisfied. "I'm putting my position, my safety, and my team's safety on the line to bring you. Don't let us down."

She faked another eager nod, but the words settled into her stomach like lead.

Just then a loud banging on the door interrupted everyone's thoughts. Tadriel sat up in his chair, doing a quick tally of everyone in the room. Maewyn, Rory, Novak, Adelia, and Ash. Everyone was here.

Novak stood first and approached the door cautiously.

"Who could it be?" Maewyn whispered.

None of them had any reason to be afraid, but Tadriel was technically in hiding. He barely left the house anymore, should he run into Wind Court royal guards.

Then sure enough, Novak looked back with alarm. She had peered under the door and whispered furiously, "Royal guard! It's the royal guard!"

A loud voice boomed from behind the door. "We know

you're in there. We can hear you. Open up now by order of the King."

"I'm opening up. One second!" She waved for everyone to go hide. Ash dragged Tadriel away from the door to find a hiding place somewhere else in the little home and Maewyn and Rory followed. Adelia tucked behind the couch. Then Novak had the door open and Adelia could barely make out two royal guards in the entranceway.

"We were told by a neighbor that this is in fact a residence, ma'am," he announced, looking around. "Thought it might be an abandoned building but..."

Novak nodded innocently. "Yes, I live here."

He looked skeptic. "But you're an Aqua?"

She pointed to the swirling gold symbol on her guard shirt. "Faerie Guard. We have safe homes all over Faerie for sanctuary. What is it that you need?" She feigned impatience.

The guard then pulled out a piece of paper from his waist-band. "We are handing out an order from the King for the return of his youngest song." He handed the paper to Novak. "If you have any contact with the youngest Prince of the Wind Court, please tell him to return to the castle immediately."

Novak looked at the paper, then back at the guard. "Uh, okay. We haven't seen him, but I'll keep it in mind."

The guard nodded. "Thanks, ma'am. Have a good day."

They left and Novak had the door closed and locked again. She threw the odd declaration for the Prince of Wind to return home on the table and looked around at everyone. Tadriel was visibly sweating, his breath hitching as he tried to come down from the panic.

"That was weird. But I think it's time we leave. All of us coming and going are bringing too much attention to Tadriel," Novak announced and everyone nodded.

. . .

IT WAS a cordial goodbye to her uncle Tad as the sun sent its last fiery kiss to the moon before it disappeared beyond the horizon. The streets were cast in a dark purple haze, and a film of mist started to creep along the roads. The shadows of the trees elongated and resembled the arms of the Molten reaching out to snatch passersby. The streets were eerily quiet, void of any laughing Fae or chirping birds.

"Please be safe, Adelia. I know you are more than capable of doing this, but just... just come back, ok?" He pulled her into a hug reminiscent of her dad's that she struggled to keep from tearing up.

"I promise. You don't have to worry about me."

She attempted to match his confidence in her, but her stomach curled at the thought of the imminent departure and the danger that awaited.

She had never told him about the key.

It was her burden and hers alone.

ADELIA and the others were taking *birds* to the Molten Court. Apparently, some Wind Fae made their living by providing what Adelia could only describe as a taxi service. She stood facing a towering ostrich, unsure how to mount it. She had never ridden a horse, let alone a bird.

And how was she supposed to stay on?

The ostrich had no saddle or reins, things she typically associated with riding.

The tasks her new companions were expecting her to do were becoming crazier and crazier. She had tried to take it in stride, but this was beyond ridiculous.

"Who do you guys think I am? Crocodile Dundee, animal wrangler extraordinaire?" She threw her hands up in exasperation and watched as Novak and Ash mounted their ostriches as if they had done it a thousand times. Ash sat poised on his with effortless grace and kept his eyes ahead as if he could see the Molten gate. She could imagine it shimmering in the fading light, keeping the riot of savage Fae from waging war on the rest of Faerie.

Rory gave a boost to Maewyn, his hands clasped to form a step for her. She catapulted onto the bird and landed softly on its feathered back. Rory gave her leg a gentle pat and went to climb onto his own.

They all had mastered the typical Fae grace; each motion was fluid and smooth.

How could she be Fae and still be so uncoordinated?

Sensing her hesitation, Adelia's ostrich knelt down before her as if giving her permission to scoot onto its soft, feathery back.

"Oh! What a gentleman." She bowed back to him. "You're much nicer than the last bird I talked to."

My pleasure, fair lady. This ostrich was definitely British. She could feel it.

She sucked in a deep breath and threw herself onto the ostrich's back, which, blessedly, was incredibly docile and remained statuesque while she positioned herself.

She wriggled herself into a semi-comfortable position and followed Ash's gaze as he looked deep into the forest.

It petrified her to think about what they were riding towards.

They were willingly going to the Molten Court, filled with Fae who had been trapped away for decades. Decades to fester in their anger and plot their revenge. She still didn't understand what had led them to practice forbidden magic, especially after learning the consequences. She couldn't comprehend how someone could be so hungry for power that they would sacrifice their sanity for it. The Molten were barely even living, surviving on their fire and hatred alone. The saddest part was they no longer even realized what they had become.

She shivered.

She may be riding towards them, but she was also riding towards her father.

Towards his salvation.

That was what would meet her across the forest on the other side of the Blacklore Woods.

She clenched fistfuls of feathers in both hands as the ostrich leapt to its feet.

They left the quiet homes of the Wind Court behind and sped toward the Blacklore Woods. The green grass waved its farewell to them as the finger-like branches of gnarled trees welcomed them. The forest seemed peaceful thus far, but she knew as they descended into the canopy, the more dangerous it would become.

With every leaping bound, it felt like she was one step closer to the gates of Hell.

CHAPTER 16

After hours of riding, her legs were sore, and her back was aching. Staying on this thing with her prosthetic leg might be one of the most difficult things she'd ever done. They finally stopped to rest for the night and she could have wept. Tomorrow, they would arrive at the mouth of the Starlight Caverns, where they would have to leave their 'rides' behind.

Adelia had taken to calling hers Camelus, after the scientific name of an ostrich.

She patted him on the back after jumping—but was more like falling—off of his back. She'd be sad to leave him behind tomorrow. After just a few hours of riding him, she had grown to love the feeling of the wind in her hair as they flew over logs and across the darkening forest floor. She followed the others and tied him to some nearby trees where he would be able to rest for the night.

"Thanks, buddy, you're the best ostrich I've ever ridden." He groaned in reply. Adelia took it as a good thing.

She moved to join the others, who had set up a small, hasty

fire.

Since firepower was only available to the Molten, they used the old-fashioned method of starting a fire with some flint Rory pulled from the earth and some branches from fallen trees scattered around them. The grove was chilly; the foliage was so thick that it was clear the sun never warmed the ground here.

The area they chose to stop was secluded, with old oaks standing guard above them like sentries. In the dense shadows, spiders clung to webs that glittered in the moonlight, and it felt as though they were watching the group. Like they were trying to figure out why these normal Fae would choose to stay in a place that permeated dark energy from every corner.

Adelia moved to sit on a lichen-covered log and noticed the array of colourful beetles skittering across the moss. Without thinking, she bent down to inspect them. Even the insects in Faerie were incredible. These ones were such vibrant shades of blue and green, and they seemed to glow in the dark.

"Everything okay over there, Adelia...?" Ash asked her curiously. He had one eyebrow cocked at her in confusion.

She realized her face was practically in the dirt and sat up quickly.

"The beetles here are quite exquisite," she said with as much bravado she could muster.

The whole team stopped what they were doing to stare at her before bursting out laughing—even Novak chuckled.

She figured it *was* pretty funny. Most people didn't think bugs were exquisite. Back at home, she had books on bugs, butterflies, and fungi lining her shelves. Beetles in particular were difficult to identify with there being so many species.

She smiled at them and shrugged. "If anyone wants to know more about beetle biology, let me know. I'd be more than happy to oblige."

Maewyn clapped her hands together in excitement. "Of

course we'd love to! I love how you appreciate the little things, Adelia. That even despite everything going on, you can look at a beetle and see beauty."

Adelia inwardly beamed. Maybe her new companions weren't fascinated by the fauna quite as much as she was, but still, they had embraced her love of it. She wasn't used to laughing *with* people instead of being laughed at. It was a nice change.

"Well, I'll take the first watch," announced Rory, standing up and brushing off his pants. "You should all get some rest."

They happily obliged and worked to make beds of moss and pine needles, thanks to Adelia's quick thinking. She appreciated how they took her ideas without question, despite not being a real part of the team.

Adelia took her leg off, smiling at Maewyn, who watched her out of the corner of her eye, and nestled into her bed. She pulled her jacket over the top of her torso, more for comfort than warmth. It gave her a sense of security. Before closing her eyes to attempt sleep, she watched as Maewyn tried to sneak over to Rory before settling into her own cot. He was fluffing up a pile of foliage to sit on at the outskirts of their little camp.

"Did you want company?" Maewyn whispered to him.

Rory shook his head. "No, no. I'm fine. Go get some sleep." He settled his back against the tree trunk and set his shield beside him.

Maewyn's face fell imperceptibly. "Oh. Okay. Yeah, of course. I wouldn't want to distract you or anything," she whispered back. Then Maewyn made her way back to her cot, and Adelia could have sworn she looked disappointed. Brushing it aside, she moved her gaze to the dying fire. Best not to keep it going all night in case it attracted unwanted visitors while the majority of them were asleep.

In a few days, she would be with her dad again, and she tried to let the positive thoughts of being reunited with him lull her to sleep.

INSTEAD, visions of blood soaking the kitchen floor bombarded Adelia's sleep. In her dreams, she tried to clean the blood away, but no matter how hard she tried, the floors remained crimson.

She'd look down at her hands and see they were stained red too.

She tried frantically to scrub the blood away, but it would just climb farther up her arms.

She was stained red up to the elbows now.

Then she'd look back up and see the bodies of Maewyn, Novak, Rory and Ash lying on the kitchen floor.

The blood was theirs.

They died by her hands, all because she had lied to get them to come on this mission.

She had walked them to the gates of Hell for her own selfish reasons. She could have given them the key and stopped the Molten already.

Their bodies were grey and cold, frozen in horrifying positions from rigor mortis. Their eyes all opened at once, white and pupilless. Their unseeing eyes bore into her.

They blamed her for killing them.

Their mouths opened, and maggots spilled out onto the kitchen floor. Horrified, Adelia tried to back away, but her limbs wouldn't move. They moved their mouths in silent words but somehow knew what they were saying.

This is your fault.

Liar.

We trusted you.

You killed us.

. . .

Adelia jolted awake from her dream, the one that had been haunting her sleep every night and only continued to get worse. The dreams were bringing all her fears to life. Her deceit was weighing heavy on her heart, and she ached to tell them about the key.

She rolled over on her makeshift cot of pine needles, surprisingly soft and warm.

She still couldn't sleep on her back as she usually would, with the burns continuing to heal. She was afraid the newly formed scabs would tear away, leaving her back exposed and vulnerable to infection.

She closed her eyes again and listened for the sounds of the forest around her. But the silence of the forest matched the silence in her soul. No crickets chirped, not a leaf rustled. She nestled into a ball to keep the heat in, except she wasn't cold as she was when they had settled in for the night. It was like her bed was sitting under a hot plate that was slowly heating up.

She scrambled up, gingerly padding the bed that was increasing in temperature. It was as if she had put it right above a hot geyser that was building up steam and ready to blow.

She touched the key at her neck to ensure it was still there and concluded that it was still the same temperature as before.

So it wasn't that.

It had to be the ground warming up. She looked over and caught a glimpse of Ash in his own cot a few metres from her.

He was thrashing.

Sweat covered his face, a look of anguish crossing his features as he tossed in his sleep. She crawled across the damp earth and sat beside him, the other two sleeping unaware around them. Rory was supposed to be on watch still. Maybe he had gotten up to relieve himself in the woods.

With the back of her hand, she tenderly felt his forehead,

shocked at its warmth. He was burning up with fever. What was going on with the forest? Was it giving them nightmares and fevers? Novak had told her to expect danger, but she hadn't prepared for the entire forest to be malicious. The air around them felt sinister. She felt like the forest had eyes and was watching her every move. Like it was slowly hoping they would descend into madness so it could trap them here forever. Soon the roots would come alive, wrap around them, and drag them all into the earth.

No. She needed to get a grip. She was projecting her fears into her surroundings. Instead, she focused on Ash.

She was pretty sure you were never supposed to wake someone up from a nightmare, especially a deadly Fae warrior who could likely knock her out in one blow.

Instead, she clasped his hand with hers, willing him to calm. She held his hand like he had done for her whenever he sensed she could use a tether.

Despite his initial cold behaviour, she found herself wanting to know more about him. She wanted to know why he was opposed to her company, and what happened to his familiar, and why he wouldn't use his powers. She wanted to know about his family and what it was like to grow up in this storybook world of monsters and magic.

She had an urge to brush her hand through his smoky grey hair to see if it was as soft as it looked. Maybe he wouldn't let her in on his dark secrets, but she would stay beside him anyway.

He began to quiet as she held his hand, his warmth seeping through the leather gloves he never took off.

The occasional fitful brow furrowing was the only indication his dreams still held him captive, and slowly Adelia felt herself drifting off to the hooting of a great horned owl at the moon.

CHAPTER 17

ASH

Ash woke with a jolt. It was a starless sky, the night air heavy around them. He had heard a faint noise off to his left, a crunching of branches and hushed voices of approaching strangers. Encountering others wandering the Blacklore Woods during the witching hours meant nothing but trouble.

He went to stand, only to find his hand grasped tightly by Adelia, who had moved to his side from her original cot across from him. She had been nestled up against his side as if trying to steal his warmth.

Confusion washed over him.

What would have possessed her to do that?

He had purposely tried to push her away over the past few days and had refused to teach her any more magic. He had tried so hard to avoid looking at her warm hazel eyes, despite the compulsion and desire he felt to stare at her all day. He tried to only steal glances at her when she was unaware of his lingering eyes.

Something about her made him want to open up and tell her all the secrets he guarded so closely.

She was determined and bright, and every time he told her they didn't need her, or that she would slow down the team, he knew it was a lie.

She had jumped into a whole new world without a backwards glance, eager to learn everything she could. It was infectious, and he wanted to be there while she learned to master the wind and even help her find her dad. It confused him how quickly he had grown to enjoy her company.

He wasn't supposed to bring new people into his life. He had Rory, Maewyn, and Novak, and that was enough. But it was hard to control himself around her—and wanting anything, even friendship, from her was dangerous.

He was dangerous.

And the last thing he wanted was to drag her down his dark path.

She was everything he wasn't, open and trusting, whereas he was closed and fearful of what would happen if he let people in.

Novak, Rory, and Maewyn were the closest he let anyone get to him since *that* day.

They knew he had secrets, but none of them had ever pressed him to confide. They had accepted him onto their team, thankful to have a strong melee fighter amongst their ranks. His choice not to use his powers had never mattered. He was as strong with his swords as they were with their elements. He had made sure of that.

He gently pulled away from Adelia, still sleeping soundly beside him, her features light and wistful, her hair a halo of blond curls around her head. She had taken off that bionic leg of hers, something she had yet to bring up with any of them. To him, it was just more proof of how strong and resilient she was. She refused to regard it as a weakness and that was inspiring.

After standing up, he bent down to push a curl away from her eyes, and she stirred slightly at his touch. He ached to lie back down and pretend he hadn't woken up, but the ominous sounds of approaching feet dragged him from her.

He grabbed his dark cloak discarded beside him and moved towards the sounds he had heard moments ago. The quiet voices grew in volume as he navigated through the damp brush, the stale odour of decomposing wood wafting up from his feet.

Sliding in behind a towering oak, he peered around it to see two Fae cautiously traversing through the brush from the west. They wore the fiery orange and black that was as dark as a moonless night, signifying they were of the Molten Court. But from what he could see, their skin was unmarred by the trace of forbidden magic.

Not every Fae had dabbled in the craft. There were many women and children who had been trapped inside the court despite having committed no crimes at all. Condemned for no reason other than being Molten.

It was a detail many Fae often forgot about or decided to never speak of. It was easy to blame the Queen and her power-hungry court for the Molten War; however, it gnawed on his conscience to think of the innocents trapped inside the gate for the crimes of their Queen.

With that said, these two didn't appear to be innocent.

The two towering men were clean-shaven, with cruel eyes peering out from behind their long black hair. They had almost as many weapons as his team did, but they definitely weren't Faerie Guards. Two twin boa constrictors slithered soundlessly through the grass behind their companions, like deadly shadows.

Just seeing them confirmed their biggest fear; the gate was down. Yes, strong Molten had escaped and attacked Adelia's house, but if these men were wandering the forest, it could only mean the gate had broken entirely. They looked strong but didn't have the strength of Fae tainted by forbidden magic. They didn't appear like they had the power to push through a semi-downed gate.

It also meant that Queen Karai would likely be assembling her army once again to march on the Wind Court. Her thirst for revenge was unquenchable, and she would relish the first opportunity in decades for retaliation on the court that had banished them.

Whether these two Fae were scouts, Ash didn't know, but he started to slink soundlessly back to rouse the others from sleep.

He woke Novak first, and the rest of the group followed, groggy-eyed and disordered. He pressed his fingers to his lips, his features urging them to stay silent.

Then he roused Rory, who he found at the edge of their camp, head lolling to the side as he sat with his back against a tree. "Seriously? You fell asleep *again?*"

Rory was the absolute worst at night shifts. Ash made a mental note to never let him do them again.

Rory shrugged apologetically and groggily stood up.

After Maewyn, Rin, and Adelia were all awake, Rory motioned for them to crowd around him. Maewyn instinctively went to Adelia to help her hop over to where Rory was motioning. He could see a look a gratitude on Adelia's face as she grabbed her leg off the ground and slung a shoulder over Maewyn. When they were all crowded together, Rory shut his eyes in concentration as he felt for the magic in the air around him. Then the earth opened up before them, creating a crater in the soft ground between the trees, which creaked slightly as the dirt shifted around their roots. A downward slope led them into the hole Rory created and Ash felt the temperature plummeting as they went below ground. Maewyn let go of Adelia, who steadied herself against the dirt wall and scurried over to the tree their ostriches had been tied to and hurried to free them all and guide them to their hideout.

The voices were growing louder, the crushing of the bushes echoing through the grove. They would be visible in less than a minute.

"Hurry up, Maewyn!" Ash whispered furiously, motioning for her to speed it up.

She scuttled as quickly as she could back through the camp with ostriches in tow, doing her best to calm the animals as she did.

Then she tripped and fell over a log around the fire. She went sprawling onto the ground, losing her grip on the ostriches, who jumped at the sudden movement.

"Damn it!" Ash bolted from the hideout and ran over to Maewyn. "Get up, get up, get up!" He roughly grabbed her under the arms and hoisted her up. He seized her hand and yanked her forward, and they sprinted as fast as they could back to the hole.

The others had grabbed the ostriches and they all descended down into the hole just as the two Fae entered the clearing.

"Now, Rory!" Novak whispered furiously.

Rory strained with the effort of lifting the dirt to create a roof for their shelter. It resulted in them being hidden below a thin layer of soil, which would be a great hiding spot unless one of the Molten walked right on top of it.

Ash could see Adelia begin to shiver in the cold and had a sudden urge to wrap his arms around her. He shook his head slightly to rid himself of the thought.

She's fine.

He needed to focus on the current situation.

Rory was struggling as it was to keep the dirt suspended mid-air to cover them.

It reminded Ash of when the four of them had been

dispatched to apprehend a Terrain Fae whose fifth wife had mysteriously disappeared.

They found the bodies of five female Fae, the last whose features weren't yet touched by decay, in deep graves in the man's backyard. The poor women had been buried alive, and Rory had absolutely raged.

He was usually so composed, a quiet, strong presence at Ash's side, but he had taken half the earth from the man's backyard and buried his house. The weak foundation of the house had collapsed under the weight, subsequently burying everything, including the man himself. Ash never asked him why that had been so triggering for him, but he knew when it came to protecting people, Rory was a force to be reckoned with. He had the utmost faith that as long as Rory was breathing, he would protect them at all costs.

The voices grew louder until he knew the Molten were no more than a few steps away. They were most likely inspecting the abandoned campsite and looting it.

No matter. They had grabbed all their essential weaponry in the seconds before hiding.

Rin was currently standing intertwined between Maewyn's feet, and he let out a low, throaty growl. Maewyn picked up the fox and whispered in hushed tones to calm him and avoid giving away their position. She looked petrified. Her fall had almost cost them. Rory reached out and wrapped his arms around Maewyn in the dark. Her eyes fluttered and she took a few steadying breaths as he held her against him.

Gruff voices broke the silence. "What ya think was going on here?" one of the Molten asked.

They heard a grunt in reply. "Did the Queen send anyone else out before us? Probably all it was. Let's keep moving. The faster we get someone and bring them back, the better. I don't want to piss off Brianka."

Then he heard a faint rustle of leaves, and Rory's face twisted in pain. A faint hiss from directly above them echoed down into the chamber.

The boa constrictor was directly above them, having slithered onto the earth Rory was balancing above their heads.

"Oy, Koa, what did you find?" the Molten with the more resonant baritone voice called to his familiar.

They heard footsteps coming closer, stopping at the edge of their pit.

Please, please, don't come any farther. Ash willed.

"There's nothing over here, you oaf. Why couldn't I have gotten a poisonous viper instead of you? The Prince's viper back at the court is deadly *and* smart." He huffed and moved away, the telltale rustle of leaves from the constrictor following close behind.

They waited in the cold dark for longer than was likely necessary. Then Rory threw the dirt up and away. Ash instinctively moved to Adelia and put an arm around her waist. She eyed him with suspicion but didn't move away.

"You good?" he asked her.

She nodded, and he couldn't help but tighten his grip around her just a bit. Then they all tentatively climbed from their hiding spot.

"Time to move on," announced Novak, voicing what they all were thinking. "I *really* don't want to encounter those snakes again." She shivered visibly.

Rory cocked an eyebrow at her. "Is the fearless Novak afraid of snakes?"

She growled.

"Oh my. You *are* afraid of snakes. How did we not know this?" He looked between Maewyn and Ash eagerly.

Novak stalked toward him. "If you *ever* tell anyone else that,

I will cut off your own little snake." She glared menacingly at him.

His smile faltered. "Scarily enough, I believe you. Lips are sealed." He mimed zipping his lips shut.

"Good. With that settled, let's head out."

Ash nodded in agreement.

The group began to pack up their scant belongings to continue their journey. Attempting to sleep again was too risky, and after that adrenaline rush, likely impossible.

Ash stole a glance over at Adelia, who after putting her leg on, was quite inelegantly trying to squirm her way back onto her ostrich. He held back a snicker and moved to climb onto his own. Somehow, he just knew it was something she'd want to accomplish without help.

In just a few days, they would be arriving at the Molten Court, and he was far from ready.

CHAPTER 18

After hours of riding, Adelia's legs were sore, and her back was aching. She wanted to tell them that she desperately needed to stop, but Novak continued to plow through the woods on her ostrich.

Rory galloped alongside Adelia, looking bored. Then he brightened and looked at her expectantly. "Why don't you try and practice, Adelia? Since we have a few more hours of riding," he asked her.

A few more hours? She inwardly groaned. She was certain she would pass out before that. "How in the world can I practice while riding?" she exclaimed. Even her teeth rattled as she spoke.

Rory smiled shyly and looked ahead. "Well, I have a fun idea."

"Oh?"

"Try making wind walls. Solid barriers of wind. I think it would be particularly amusing if you made one in front of Ash."

She couldn't help but snicker and stole a glance at Ash, who trotted ahead, out of earshot.

"But I wouldn't want to hurt his ostrich."

"Then make the wind wall between the ostrich's head and Ash. So he gets knocked off."

"So you're telling me to clothesline Ash with wind?" she asked incredulously.

Rory looked at her, confused. "I have no idea what that means."

Adelia shook her head. "You are diabolical, Rory. Who knew." But she nodded. This *would* be fun.

She took a deep breath and reached out with her mind. Instantly, she could feel the air particles around them, waiting for her instructions. She imagined them forming a barrier, coalescing around Ash. As she held her hand out, the air around them came to her call. Calling the wind was becoming easier every time she practiced. She imagined forming a small barrier in front of Ash.

She felt the particles obey and then *OOMPH*.

Ash's face thunked against the invisible barrier and he fell backwards off the ostrich. His ostrich kept running, completely oblivious to its lost rider. Ash hit the ground hard, sprawled out on his back in the dirt.

He groaned and sat up gingerly. "Bloody hell. What in the Orb was that?" He rubbed the side of his face and looked around for the object he had run into.

Rory and Adelia howled with laughter.

Adelia's ostrich slowed as she reached him and she smiled sweetly. "I'm so sorry. I was practicing my barriers and I'm not very good at placing them where I want yet."

He scowled. "Bullshit."

"You'll never know, I guess." She shrugged.

Rory chuckled and gave his ostrich the go-ahead to continue. It trotted off to follow Novak and Maewyn, while Adelia tried to school her features back to neutrality.

"Do you realize you're going to have to share yours now?" Ash crossed his arms and flashed her his own sweet smile.

"Wait. What do you mean?"

He pointed to his ostrich, who was still running away from them. "You knocked me off, so now you get to share your ostrich with me. There is no way in hell I'm walking the rest of the way." He stood up and tried to brush the dirt from his hair.

"Oh no. That wasn't part of the deal."

Ash chuckled and without waiting for her permission leapt gracefully onto the back of the ostrich. He slid in behind her and she could feel all the places he was pressed up against her more acutely than ever. His legs rubbing against hers, and the rise and fall of his chest against her back.

"You know what? This might actually be fun," he breathed into her ear and Adelia shivered. His powerful frame engulfed her as he slid his arms around her, tucking her into his chest.

"Can you please scoot back a bit?" she coughed out.

"No can do, Goldilocks. There's not much space on this bird."

"Of course there's not," she muttered.

"I'm starting to think you knocked me off on purpose. You wanted me to ride with you, didn't you?"

"No! I knocked you off because I thought it would be funny to see you so caught off guard. And I succeeded in that at least."

Her heart thundered as the ostrich started moving again, trying to catch up with the others. She hoped the bumpy ride would hide her racing pulse. He was too close and she couldn't think straight.

He lifted a hand and brushed his fingers softly across the taut cords in her neck. Adelia quickly batted away his hands.

"Stop that! I didn't give you permission to caress my neck."

"It's just that you're so tense, Adelia. You're going to be sore after riding if you don't learn how to relax your muscles while you ride," he said into her ear.

Huh. Maybe he had a point. She was already incredibly sore. She tried to relax a little bit, but in doing so found herself leaning back slightly into Ash. His body was hard but warm. As she leaned back slightly, his arm tightened around her waist a tad.

"See? Now isn't that better?"

"No," she grumbled. "I hate this."

He smirked against her ear. "Keep telling yourself that."

CHAPTER 19

Adelia hated to admit riding with Ash had been enjoyable. The time flew by and before she knew it, they found themselves staring at a behemoth opening to a dark cave. The yellows and reds of the sunrise leaked into the sky like watercolour, and the ill-boding sense of the forest dissipated. The scenery around them had begun to change a few hours ago as the knotted trees around them thinned out. She could see mountains looming in the distance, their bone-white jagged peaks blotting the horizon.

A thick mist hovered at the base of the mountains, obscuring the passageway Novak said weaved through them. Their path to the court was through these caverns, the Starlight Caverns, Novak had told her.

The name was contradictory because, despite Novak's warnings, they sounded beautiful and intriguing. She felt drawn to explore inside, to see why they were named after the night sky.

She and her dad had explored caverns near Bark Beach once, with only their flashlights and helmets. There was a thick layer of bedrock all along Bark Beach, and there were some areas where it had collapsed. They called them windows.

Once you found a window, you could drop down below the bedrock and explore the maze of tunnels that only the spiders knew about. The dark passageways would open up into massive underground caverns tall enough even to stand in.

She had taken her flashlight and camera in and catalogued each spider for future research. It was a nature-lover's heaven. She was dripping with anticipation now to see what kinds of wonders lurked in the underground world of Faerie. Maybe that made her foolish, but she was ok with that.

THEY LET their ostriches go at the cave entrance. Novak said they were trained to return home and would be fine. Adelia gave Camelus one last awkward pat on the back before sending him off, and then they descended into the rocky womb.

The first thing that hit Adelia was the smell. She had expected a typical dank, mossy, wet smell. Instead, the cavern permeated an intoxicating aroma of cranberries and ocean breezes. The caverns reminded her of home, of her dad's baking and sitting on the porch reading a book.

She smiled to herself.

It was exactly what she needed, a reminder of why she was here. What she was fighting for. She unconsciously slowed her walking pace, wondering where the smell could be coming from down here.

Ash matched her pace and fell into step beside her. He looked at her with concern. "Keep your wits about you, Adelia. The caverns are magical. They prey on your senses. The first thing they'll try and do is assault your sense of smell. They make you smell something that comforts you, to entice you to go farther in."

"What do you smell?" she asked curiously.

Magic be damned, she was feeling lighter already than she was before. The stress that had been gnawing at her soul was dissipating with the wind. It was a freeing feeling, and she was going to try and hold onto it. As long as she stayed aware of the effects it was having on her, and alert of her surroundings, she would be fine.

He paused before replying, as if trying to place the fragrances assaulting his own senses.

"Hmm, I smell leather... and honey-jasmine perfume." He smiled to himself sadly and glanced back at her.

Honey-jasmine perfume? Maybe a lover's? She hated the pang she felt at the thought.

Maewyn, who had been eavesdropping, chipped in, "Oo-la-la, perfume, Ash? Do you have someone back at the Wind Court we don't know about?" She sounded hurt at the prospect that he had someone special back home and hadn't told them.

He chuckled darkly. "No, nothing like that, Mae. Don't worry, you'll be the first to know *if* that ever happens."

"Has it ever happened?" Adelia blurted out, curiosity getting the better of her. She kicked herself as soon as she spoke. His love life was *certainly* none of her business.

"Why, Adelia? Jealous? Or just curious what it'd be like to be with me?" He smiled seductively, his caramel eyes darkening. She couldn't help but notice the way his pants hugged him in all the right places as he swaggered along beside her.

Her cheeks heated, but he continued, "I'm sure those human boys would pale in comparison to being with a Fae."

Adelia's steps faltered, crimson flooding her cheeks.

Oh, God.

This isn't happening.

I need to think before speaking.

He stopped with her and leaned closer to her. "And I'd be more than happy to show you," he purred in her ear.

He brought his fingers up to her face, and with featherlight touch, ran them behind her ear and down her neck.

She shivered. She couldn't help the onslaught of images that flooded her mind. Of what it would be like to be with a Fae. *To be with him.*

She coughed to herself, mostly to rid the visions. "No, thank you, I have someone at home." Not true at all, but it felt good to say regardless. "I'm sure your ego keeps you warm at night, anyway."

His attitude towards her was so hot and cold, she couldn't keep track of it. She was not about playing games.

He chuckled at her comment, and then Novak barked at them to catch up.

THE TEMPERATURE DROPPED the farther they descended into the caves, sending violent chills down Adelia's spine. The light never reached the ceiling or walls down here, and their sight was confined to the small circles of orange light cast by the sconces along the walls. She assumed they had been enchanted with Molten magic to burn forever. It served as an eerie reminder of where they were headed and the power the Molten had. Adelia could hear the odd drip of water onto the cavern floor, but when she looked up, all she saw were jagged teeth of stone descending from the shadows above.

The caves were devoid of life as far as she could see, and that worried her more than anything else. If not even the spiders wanted to dwell here, then maybe Novak's warning about the dangers here were true.

She was leading the way with Ash now, a comfortable silence settling between them. Any time she drifted off in thought, she caught herself thinking about what it would feel like to run her hands through his hair. Then she'd scold herself and focus on walking instead.

She didn't like this new feeling while being near him. Walking beside him made her fidgety, yet at ease at the same time. She tried to keep her eyes on the path ahead; with her luck, she'd steal a glance at him and trip and fall. She'd *never* hear the end of that.

"Can we take a water break? I'm parched," Rory asked, interrupting her thoughts.

"Might as well. We still have a ways to go." Novak shrugged off her pack and found a boulder to sit and rest on.

Adelia had to agree. They had been walking for hours and she was already feeling achy. She didn't want to be the one to make the suggestion first, compelled to prove herself worthy of being brought along.

They all sat on boulders or on the floor, forming a little circle.

Adelia pulled a skin from her pack and took a sip. The cool water slid down her throat, and she sighed. Rory was gulping down his water with ardor, and she looked at him skeptically.

"Shouldn't you save some of that, Rory?"

"Novak can make us more, no worries. Drink your fill." He gave her a warm smile in return.

She had completely forgotten Novak could use her powers. Being around Fae was quite handy.

"Will you tell me about Queen Karai?" Adelia asked after taking a hearty gulp this time. Thus far her knowledge of the Queen of the Molten Fae was limited. All she knew was that she was the Mother Gothel of this fairy tale, aka the evil villain who was power-hungry and just a bit insane.

Novak pulled out air cakes from her bag and passed them around the circle before she began. Rory graciously accepted his and ate the whole thing in one bite before Novak had even started. "Queen Karai has been ruler of the Molten Fae for a century. She is the only female ruler, the other courts being ruled by Kings. History says she was once a fair and just queen. But then she decided ruling over one court wasn't enough. She wanted more. I, for one, admired her ambition, but she went a little too far. She began to practice forbidden magic to grow stronger so that she could overthrow the other courts. She decided to take down the Wind Court first, their king having been known for his frivolity and lackadaisical attitude in terms of ruling his court."

Adelia nodded. She knew as much about the forbidden magic and its effects.

"Under the influence of forbidden magic, she became unhinged. She brainwashed her court with grandiose ideas of power and glory, and soon most Fae in the court had joined her in practicing forbidden magic. You have to remember, though, that doing forbidden magic comes at a cost—to yourself and the person you steal the magic from. So in order to become powerful, she sacrificed the lives of her own people to steal their power. In doing so, she became even more unhinged, unpredictable, and ruthless."

So avoid running into the Queen at all costs then? Sounded like a plan to Adelia.

Adelia was about to ask more when Rory paused in his cake eating.

He held up his hands for them all to do the same, and Adelia froze mid-drink.

"Shh… do you hear that?" he whispered.

They all paused, and Adelia strained her ears.

Then she heard it, a faint rumble.

CHAPTER 20

ASH

Ash was deep in thought, chiding himself for flirting so shamelessly with Adelia. He was angry at his callousness and inability to keep his distance, when Rory called for silence.

As soon as the shuffling of their movements and quiet chatter had faded into the darkness, he heard it as well. A faint rumbling had begun above their heads. He knew there had been cave-ins here before but had hoped they would be lucky enough to avoid one.

Tremors began around their feet, sending vibrations through their soles and rattling their teeth. He looked around to try and find somewhere they could hide, but the tunnel they were in was barren, save for the couple boulders they were sitting on, the cold stone walls, and the stalactites dripping down from the ceiling. The stalagmites would soon skewer them if they didn't get out of here.

"Scatter!" yelled Novak.

He made to move, but before even having a chance to react, the roof above them cracked like a mouth yawning open, and stone began to rain down on them. Chunks of the ceiling dropped to the floor and exploded, sending shrapnel flying across the tunnel's width. The vibrations increased until just trying to stand upright was a challenge.

"Come on! We need to get out of here." He grabbed Adelia, pulling her forward into the cave, away from a large chunk of stone that missed where she had been standing by a few steps. The others jumped back, narrowly avoiding the mass of falling debris collapsing around them.

Ash could see some chunks of rocks being slowed mid-air as Rory tried to use his powers to keep the cave from collapsing altogether and give them a chance to escape. It was clear that it was more than he could handle, though. The weight of an entire tunnel was too much. He was visibly straining with the effort and only managed to slow or break apart the larger chunks that threatened to hit them.

Ash stumbled ahead, pulling Adelia alongside him. They were dodging flying bits of stone with less success as the collapse progressed. He felt some scatter across his shoulder, ripping his cloak and skin underneath.

He picked up the pace. "Faster, Adelia!" They needed to get out of this section before they were buried alive.

But Adelia resisted him instead and paused. She looked conflicted as to whether to follow him or stay where she was.

"What are you doing?" he bellowed.

She'd be killed if she stopped. They might still be crushed even if they kept moving forward. The stone raining down around them was unrelenting and progressing farther and farther along the tunnel.

Then out of the blue, she shoved him.

Hard.

Adelia clearly put every last bit of her strength into pushing him, which was the last thing he was expecting. Ash lost his balance and fell to the floor. Adelia tumbled with him, and he tried to fling out his arms to catch their fall.

He hit the ground, and she fell on top of him. As soon as they did, she flung out her hands, and a protective bubble of wind materialized around them. It was a thin dome encapsulating them inside. The debris raining down around them hit the barrier and bounced off, leaving them unharmed.

Ash realized she wanted them close to the ground and close to each other so that she didn't have to create a large dome—she wasn't that strong yet. It was actually brilliant.

Her face was screwed up in concentration, her breathing becoming laboured with every second she protected them from the avalanche of stone.

He should be helping her, but he couldn't really move even if he wanted to. She was on top of him.

Wait, she was on *top* of him.

He hadn't realized just how close they were because it had felt so natural, despite the dire situation. She was straddling him, her legs draped over the sides of his body. He had his hand wrapped around her waist protectively from the fall and ached to pull her closer. But her hands were extended up to keep the bubble around them and she was thoroughly distracted with saving their lives.

While he was incredibly distracted thinking about taking her in this position.

Eventually, the vibrations ceased, and the debris raining down relented.

She opened her eyes, and he saw a visible flush creep across her neck as she quickly pushed herself up off him and dusted herself off.

"You're welcome," she tried to say haughtily.

He slowly got to his feet, brushing the debris off himself as well.

"You ruined my new cloak, but I guess I can look past it." His cloak was almost brown from the dirt and ripped at the shoulder.

Adelia looked absolutely ready to murder him. Good. She *should* hate him.

"You ungrateful asshole."

He smirked and stepped closer to her. "What? If I actually told you that you were brilliant and resourceful, you might actually start liking me."

"No need to worry about that," she spat back out at him.

"Hmm, are you sure? If I didn't know better, I would've thought you liked riding me like that."

Her face lit up fiery red. "I was not *riding* you!"

Oh, she is too easy to bait like this.

"No, I guess you weren't. You'd be screaming my name, not screaming in fear."

"Oh my God, you're so indecent!" She whirled away from him. Definitely to try and hide the blush he could *clearly* see. "We need to find the others. Make sure they are okay. And I was most definitely not screaming in fear either. Don't exaggerate."

They surveyed the damage around them.

The tunnel they had been moving through had fully collapsed. Before them was a wall of stone now blocking the way back. That wasn't the worst part, though. Novak, Rory, and Maewyn were nowhere to be seen.

They were trapped on the other side.

CHAPTER 21

Adelia froze at the sight of the devastating tunnel collapse behind her. The rubble now blocked the pathway, separating them from the others.

She ran over to the rocks and began trying to move them out of the way. She could dig a hole through and reach them, and Rory would be able to assist from the other side. He had *magic*, after all. She scraped her fingers against the stone frantically, trying to dig her way to the other side. Her nails chipped, and dirt coated her hands as she dug and dug. It wouldn't take that long, and she couldn't just leave them.

But why isn't Ash helping?

Ash came up behind her then and rested a hand on her shoulder. "It's too much, Adelia. Take a step back. Just *look*."

Frustrated, she obliged and took a moment to actually survey the damage. There were stones the size of cars piled to the ceiling, not even a sliver to the other side visible through the mass. She also knew if Rory could help, he would, which was even more concerning. There was a good chance he was injured if he wasn't working to clear a path through for them.

"Well then… what do you suggest?" she whispered.

"We keep moving. Novak and the others will have to take the mountain pass around the caverns. We will meet them at the exit."

"Didn't you say the way through the mountains was danger-ous, and we should avoid that?"

"Yes." He paused and ran a hand through his silvery hair in frustration. "But we don't have any other options. They can handle it."

She nodded. She saw sense in his logic, even if she didn't like it.

She wheeled around to grab her pack and realized with horror it was nowhere around. They had all taken off their packs before the collapse had occurred… which meant their food, supplies, extra weapons, *everything*—was buried.

She and Ash resigned themselves to the fact that they would have to continue through the caverns without their packs. There was only one exit, and they should be able to make it out of the caverns by tomorrow if they moved swiftly.

Hopefully, once back outside, they could forage for food that would be safe to eat. Until then, no water and no food.

They walked in an uneasy silence, both of them still reeling from the cave-in and separation from the others. Adelia knew if she was worried about them, then Ash must be worried signifi-cantly more. They were his team and she didn't know if he had ever travelled without them.

They passed stone wall after stone wall, all the boulders and thin crevasses blending into one as they wove down the passage.

He was the first to break the silence. "Did you know that before the Molten War, these caverns were the main passageway for travelling Molten Fae to get to the Wind Court and vice versa?"

"So I guess there was a time in history where the Wind and Molten Fae got along?"

He seemed thoughtful for a moment. "Generations ago, they did. They were allies. They had trade agreements and came to each other's courts for celebrations. The Wind Court has a massive festival every year to honour the birds. Fae wear various bird masks, and the food and drink is spectacular. Fae from all the other courts used to travel days to Zephyr for the festival. We still celebrate, but I've never seen anyone from another court make an appearance. Faerie is a broken world."

"But you, Novak, Rory, and Maewyn are all different Fae?"

"The Guard is the only place where any intermingling occurs. It's only because having a variety of Fae increases our success on missions."

"Why do you think it's like that?" she asked. "The hesitancy to intermingle, I mean."

"I think it has to do with the kings and queens. They got so caught up in being the strongest and began to look down at other types of Fae. They tried to instill a belief in their people that the other Fae are lesser. A rift formed. It's hard to overcome that when each court believes they are better. I think the world has forgotten what it was like to be united."

"That really doesn't sound so different from the human world."

As they walked along the tunnels, Adelia spotted old signs of use from when the Molten travelled the tunnels. The odd broken discarded lantern or forgotten canteen of water. Not that there was any water left in them—she certainly checked. Her mouth was parched, her thirst becoming distracting, but Ash kept walking. He seemed determined to reach some mysterious destination unbeknownst to her.

Minutes became hours, and eventually time lost all meaning. She could not rely on the sun, so she gauged how much time had passed by the soreness in her feet. She could feel an ache in her soles and relished the thought of stopping for the night. Her tongue was sticky against the roof of her mouth. She figured her excessive thirst was due to a combination of exercise and the dry, stale air in the tunnels.

As Adelia began to wonder how far Ash would take them, the tunnel began to widen.

"We're stopping up ahead for the night," he announced, and she could hear in his voice how dry his throat was as well.

The tunnel continued to widen until it opened into a massive cavern. The ceilings were at least thirty feet high, and the entire room fifty feet wide. The centre of the room was a sparkling pool of dark water that reflected an otherworldly blue glow around the pathway around it. The path itself wove around the water in a giant circle. Upon closer inspection, the cavern ceiling above them was dotted with thousands of glowing blue lights. They sparkled like the stars in the night sky, casting the cave in an eerie blue haze.

Bioluminescence.

Adelia knew a few creatures back in the human realm had the ability, but these were like nothing she had ever seen. The longer she stared in awe at the ceiling, she began to realize the slight shift in colours. The glow turned from a dark midnight blue to a soft cerulean blue, and

then began to shift into tones of seafoam green. The ombre colours of green and blue reflected onto the sparkling water below, making the dark, depthless water come alive.

She marveled at the beauty of the cavern and now understood why they called it the Starlight Caverns.

"What *is* this?" she said in awe.

"These are the blushing dragonflies. Fae used to travel here from all over Faerie to see them. It's said that if one lands on you, it imbues you with its light, and you will have good luck for the next year."

"How do I get one to land on me?" She laughed. "I could use a bit of luck."

She didn't say it was because they were going to the Molten Court. He already knew they could use all the luck they could get.

She watched, mesmerized, as a dragonfly parted with the ceiling and floated down towards them, leaving a trail of glowing dust behind it. It looked like an ultraviolet shooting star streaking across the cavern. It floated past her head and she reached out tentatively to touch it but only managed to brush her hand through the trail of dust.

She looked back at Ash, disappointed, but he was struggling to keep a straight face. Then he burst out laughing.

"What? What's so funny?"

He reached out his hand and lightly brushed her nose, and his black glove came away blue.

"You got a little dragon dust on you."

His smile was so pure, so unadulterated that it made her heart flip. It reminded her of how he was back at The Perch.

She looked around them and saw a pile of the dust on the ground. Adelia bent down and scooped it up into her palms and blew it right at his face.

It exploded in a cloud of glowing blue powder all around him.

She giggled when it dispersed and he was blue and glowing.

"Oh, you'll pay for that," he growled back, a smile still tugging at his lips.

He lunged, but she darted away, laughing. Ash was faster, though, and despite her best efforts to escape, he soon had her enveloped in his arms. He took the chance to smear his glowing hands across her face.

"No!" She tried to protest between the laughter, and he finally let her go.

They were both covered in the ultraviolet dust, glowing blue in the dark cavern.

"You're as radiant as the sun," he said with a smile and carefully brushed a curl out of her eyes.

"And you are glowing like you're radioactive... this is safe, right?"

He chuckled. "With a name like blushing dragonflies, how could they be dangerous?"

"I hope you're right. It'd be a shame to die now."

"Indeed. Shall we go rest our legs for a little bit then, my glowing star?"

She smiled back at him and nodded.

Ash moved to sit down on the stone floor. They didn't have their packs with them, but he took off his cloak and laid it down on the floor to offer some protection from the chill. Then he stretched down onto it, resting his arms behind his head as he relaxed for the first time in hours.

It was such a relief that they had stumbled across the water. Clearly, that was why Ash hadn't been concerned at all before. He knew they would stop here for the night and drink their fill from the glossy lake.

She knelt down beside the black waters and ran her hand through the surface, causing little waves to ripple out across its expanse. She couldn't see the bottom, but the water looked clean and untainted. The water itself seemed to be calling out to her, whispering at her in seductive, hushed tones. She had an urge to strip down and dive into the waters and wash away the blue powder covering her skin. She wondered what it would feel like to have the glossy water run through her hair and imagined it would be wonderful to rid herself of the grime and debris from the cave-in.

Come closer. The water seemed to whisper to her, and she wondered idly if Ash heard it too. They could go swimming in the pool together. Wash away all the worries, the stress, the obligations weighing them down.

I can take your burdens away, the water seemed to say.

She wanted that so badly.

She had felt so much over the past few days. Her heart was constantly full of dread, full of worry, and she needed to cleanse it from her soul. She could start over again.

Everything will be fine. The water caressed her with its words.

And she knew it would.

If she got into the water, she could forget all the bad things that had happened. She wouldn't have to worry again. Life would be full of careless laughter, seductive whispers, and easy smiles. And she didn't need anything else, did she? She didn't need anything else in life but the warm caress of this water.

First, she needed to drink, though. Then she would swim.

She bent down and formed a cup with her hands, filling it with the warm, black water. Some of the liquid leaked out between her fingers as she brought it to her mouth and took a sip.

THE WORLD EXPLODED into a psychedelic rainbow of blues and greens as her senses reached out farther than she ever thought possible. The small details of the cave around her shifted into focus—each atom of dirt on the ground, each droplet of water clinging to the walls. Effervescent smells assaulted her nose, so rich that it was like she could taste the air. It smelled like cranberries and ocean breezes, like when she had first entered the cave. She was relieved to have finally found the source. She stuck her tongue out like she was catching snowflakes to taste the sweet fruit.

Adelia stared in awe around her as the creatures on the ceiling came alive. They wriggled around on the ceiling like bees, and one by one, they took off and began to float around her. They looked like blue and green fireflies. She reached out to touch them, but they were always just out of reach. She felt like she was inside an incandescent snow globe, surrounded by shimmering creatures that defied gravity in the way they sailed through the air. They looked like butterflies floating in the wind, but there was no wind down here.

When she caught sight of her hands, she realized she was glowing like the creatures were. She could see her aura, and it shone a brilliant turquoise green.

She felt beautiful.

She spun around in a joyous circle, watching the trails of light from her fingers leave streams in the air.

She soaked in the wonderland around her and realized the water was not a stagnant black—it was alive. It moved and swirled in a hypnotizing pattern that called out to her again. It looked warm and inviting, and she couldn't wait another moment before getting into the water.

But then she heard someone calling her name from behind her.

They sounded frantic, worried even.

She thought they probably needed to swim in the water too.

She began to lift her shirt up to take it off. She knew she couldn't swim with clothes on. That would be silly.

She felt hands grab hers and try to stop her from taking it off.

Why would someone stop her? Was it that person who needed to swim too?

"Are you coming swimming with me?" she asked.

"No! You can't go swimming, Adelia!" His muffled far-away voice echoed in her ears.

She furrowed her eyebrows. "Why not?"

"That water is dangerous. It will *kill* you."

She laughed. "No, it won't!"

She turned around to face the mysterious person. He had warm caramel eyes and soft grey hair that had taken on a slightly blue tinge from the glow of the creatures above. He was tall and muscular. She stared at him, and a small feeling in the back of her mind tried to tell her something. It felt like she knew him but couldn't remember how or why she did.

Not that it mattered.

She was about to go swimming in the pool, and a beautiful man was standing in front of her. He could go swimming too. They could swim and bask in the glow while the lake whispered to them.

The waters could take the worries of this stranger too.

His face was a tight mask of concern, but her gaze quickly drifted down. He was wearing a tight-fitted black shirt, and she could see the definition of his chest, shoulders, and arms beneath it.

She reached out to touch him. She brushed featherlight fingers across his chest, trailing her finger down... down... down, and he sucked in a breath with the contact.

She liked that noise.

She wanted to make him do it again.

But then he caught her hands and stopped her.

Why did he stop her?

She saw his mouth move as if he was trying to say something to her, but it was like he was trying to talk to her underwater. She could hear the muffled sounds of a language being spoken, but it sounded far away.

All she knew was that he seemed worried. She could tell by the look on his face, the fear in his eyes.

He tried to pull her away from the water, and she bucked.

She wanted to go swimming.

He dragged her away from the lake, still calling her name, to the walls of the cavern and placed her down between two large boulders. He sat down in front of her, his taller body easily blocking her.

She tried to scoot past him, but he held fast, cutting her way back to the pool.

Why was he doing this? Didn't he know she wanted to go swimming?

The man took her hands in his and held them there.

It distracted her. The feeling was comforting. But why did he have gloves on? It would surely feel better to hold his hands without them.

She moved to take off the gloves. He couldn't swim with them anyway.

But again, he stopped her.

This was becoming annoying.

He just didn't understand the need she felt to submerge herself beneath the inky darkness of the lake. She needed to feel the thick water close over her head and sink below the surface. She knew the water would embrace her. It would take away all her worries and hold her. The water knew she needed to be held right now.

She heard him trying to talk in his far-away voice again, but it seemed more muffled than before. Whatever he was saying seemed important.

Maybe she would sit with him for a few minutes then.

Maybe she could even convince him to come swimming with her too.

CHAPTER 22

MAEWYN

You *may be small, but you are mighty. You can bring the world to its knees around you and show them what it means to underestimate you. Your might will help you conquer any obstacle before you. Your power comes from within.*

Maewyn repeated the manta her mother spoke to her years ago as she struggled with Novak to get Rory out of the caves.

Rory's entire body weight rested on their shoulders and he was no small Fae.

Maewyn's knees buckled under the immense pressure every few steps, but she would not let him fall.

Her mother knew she'd spend her life being underestimated for her size, so she made up for it in sheer willpower, something she had an abundance of.

Rory had been so preoccupied with trying to stop the falling debris during the cave-in from falling on his friends that he lost sight of protecting himself. Maewyn had watched it happen as if it were in slow motion. A colossal rock had broken free from the ceiling, and with a sickening crack, struck Rory over the head.

He had collapsed to the ground, moaning. It hadn't knocked him unconscious—she swore his skull was made of stone sometimes—but he was sufficiently dazed and confused.

He couldn't connect the threads of his mind to his legs to tell them to get back up and *move*.

She and Novak had taken an absolute beating while trying to escape because of having to drag Rory behind them. Rin had been sweet and tried to help drag him, but foxes were known for their agility, not their strength.

Now Maewyn was covered in dust and grime, and her skin was littered in countless of gashes from falling shards of stone.

Her skin was so peppered with red lesions that a passerby would have mistaken it for the winter plague. Rory had eventually regained some of his ability to walk but was unsteady and groggy. She knew he had a concussion. He kept squeezing his eyes shut forcefully every few minutes as if willing the world to stop spinning around him.

All she could do was whisper in soothing tones that everything would be okay. She channeled the voice her mother used when she had stubbed her toe or bumped her head as a child. *Shhh, Maewyn. Calm your worry. It will pass.*

And it would.

This was just another obstacle they had to overcome.

One doesn't do well to dwell on troubles but should trouble themselves with how to overcome them instead, her mother's voice echoed in her head.

There was nothing they could have done to shift the mountain of earth blocking their path without his help.

So she picked him up off the floor, dusted him off, and began to make their way back to the cave's entrance. They would have to go through the mountain pass instead.

They stopped to rest once they had made it to the cave's entrance, feeling defeated. They had been travelling for so long, only to end up back where they started, with Rory injured and separated from Ash and Adelia.

Although she couldn't deny she liked the thought of those two finally spending some time alone together.

Somehow, Adelia had been slowly chiselling away at Ash's hardened exterior, breaking away the cold, hard shell he kept up even around them. Despite knowing him for years, she still felt like she barely knew him at all.

"Do you think they are going to be ok?" she asked no one in particular. She knew Novak would say yes and wasn't disappointed.

"Of course. Ash could handle the caverns alone if he needed, but he's got Adelia too. They'll keep each other alive. Don't ever think for a second they won't be ok." Her cobalt gaze bore into Maewyn, and she almost felt guilty for asking, for doubting them.

"It's just... the caves are dangerous."

"Don't forget the path we have to take now, Maewyn."

She nodded. None of them had travelled through the mountains before. It was uncharted territory.

She tried to plaster a smile on her face regardless. "Feeling up to it?" She gave Rory a sombre smile.

He grinned back. "I was born of rock and earth Mae. I can handle a measly mountain pass."

"Good thing. If you weren't so thick-skulled, that cave-in might have killed you."

He chuckled and tapped on his skull lightly. "Thicker than the earth's crust, I assure you."

"Does that mean you're admitting to being bone-headed?"

He scoffed. "I'm offended! And here I thought you considered me the smartest, most level-headed one of the group." He leaned over to shove her playfully with his shoulder.

His small shove was enough to knock her over and she fell to the ground with a yelp.

They both broke out laughing as he helped pull her back to her feet again and dust her off.

"Thick-skulled and violent!" She laughed back. "A dangerous combination."

"One would think being dangerous was a good thing in our profession."

"You know what's even more dangerous? Being little and dangerous, so people underestimate you all the time." She shoved him back, hard enough he went stumbling into Novak, who glared at them with daggers.

"I thought you had a concussion?" Novak accused Rory.

He squinted at her. "Oh, I'm sure I do. My head is throbbing, I'm dizzy, and there are three of you right now. But I'm trying to stay positive."

Maewyn smothered a smile, and she felt lighter as they turned towards the colossal mountains looming around them. If Rory was well enough to joke around with her, then they could continue on their way.

She gazed up at the mountains surrounding the mouth to the cavern, their tall bone-white peaks reaching up in worship to the sun. A cool breeze came down from the summits the closer they got.

It reminded her of home in the Snow Court.

She embraced the chilly kiss on her cheeks and the way the air seemed fresher. She inhaled deeply so the frosty air would coat her lungs, feeling rejuvenated.

She glanced over at Rory, who was steadier on his feet now, but still not as graceful as usual. He was walking a little like Adelia, she thought, and chuckled at herself.

Then the wind started to pick up, as did the incline they were walking along. Maewyn could feel the steady burn begin in her quads with each step closer to the cloud line. She hoped Rory could handle it, but he also wasn't the type to admit defeat easily. He probably already felt guilty enough for getting injured and failing to recover Ash and Adelia from the cave-in.

She stole another glance at him, and sure enough, tiny beads of sweat dusted his forehead despite the wintry wind. His jaw was clenched, and she swore he was doing his best to conceal his laboured breathing. To be fair, though, he was twice her height and three times her size, which was a lot more weight to carry up a mountain. Terrain Fae were built like the earth they commanded; his body was refined but solid. His broad shoulders took up more than half the width of the narrow path they climbed.

Visibility slowly decreased as they climbed higher and higher, and eventually, they were swallowed up into the mountain mist. It was so thick that it consumed the sounds around them, enveloping them in a cocoon of perpetual grey deafness. The skeletal fingers of fear crept up her spine. She instinctively reached out for Rory beside her as it grew heavier, craving an anchor in the dense, cloying mist. She figured his height might give him an advantage since the mist was thicker closer to the ground.

She fumbled around, trying to find his back so she could latch onto his shirt and let him lead the way, but instead, she brushed what she assumed was his hand. Maewyn instinctively went to pull away, but his hand caught her and held tight.

It felt odd but comforting.

She had never held hands with anyone before. She stuck to hugs. And Maewyn hugged *everyone*.

It was never anything more than a greeting to her, even for strangers she met.

But this felt different.

Holding his hand felt intimate. She knew it meant nothing,

but the comfort and support she needed radiated from him. He brushed his thumb occasionally across the back of her hand, which sent her heart jumping.

Ash would have never held her hand like this. He would have tolerated her keeping a hand on his back not to get lost, but he would never be her anchor like Rory was right now. It felt almost taboo.

Because this was *Rory*.

He didn't have feelings for her.

He was just a good friend.

But despite trying to tell herself this meant nothing, she found herself hoping that even if the fog dispersed, he wouldn't let go.

As they trekked tirelessly, Maewyn looked up to notice peculiar small, orange flecks of light ahead. Their orange glow pulsed through the mist like beacons.

"What's that...?" she asked cautiously and lifted her hand to point at the specks through the haze to Rory and Novak.

Rory paused. "I'm not sure..."

A piercing moan echoed through the fog ahead and another chill scurried up her back and into her head, taking her rational thoughts hostage.

What in the Orb was hidden within the mist? A fire-breathing dragon? A camp full of Molten Fae?

She knew dangerous creatures lurked in the shadows of the mountain passages, but it was hard to know what awaited them when the mist was so thick.

But there was only one path. They had to keep moving.

As they neared, she noticed it was more than just a few lights. There were hundreds of little orange spots the size of thimbles that dotted the landscape. Some of the orange flecks flickered and sputtered like they were dancing in the wind.

That's when she realized—they were fires.

Novak drew her sword from its sheath silently while Rory moved his bulky shield to cover both himself and Maewyn.

She glanced at him gratefully.

Maewyn prepped her own magic and felt a small shard of ice form in both of her hands. The cold bit at her skin, but it was always a welcome feeling. One of comfort much like that of Rory's hands. It was odd that both the frozen touch of her ice and the warm caress of Rory's hands were so comforting. It was a paradox, but she couldn't deny how both eased her soul in very different ways.

She pulled more magic from the air, and the ice shard grew until she held two jagged daggers in her palms. Rin growled beside her, matching her unease.

Rory, Novak, and Maewyn focused on lightening their steps as they approached cautiously, unaware of what horror might await them ahead. The fog began to clear as they proceeded closer to the mysterious orange flecks. They moved silently, the sound of their breathing hidden by the whistling winds as they emerged from the deafening cocoon of fog.

Eventually, Maewyn caught sight of the light source—small crackling fires that were indeed so small, they would barely reach her ankles.

Around each one sat *sprites*.

She dropped her arms to her sides, completely baffled by the sight. It wasn't even the fire that was odd. It was the sprites themselves. Up in these desolate mountains, she would have expected to find snow sprites, but these were... fire sprites?

Sprites generally lived in each court and assisted the Fae in many ways. For years, the sprites and Fae had lived in harmony; she had even grown up beside them in her household. The sprite that had lived in the Snow castle with her was named Kikaleen and she was a healer.

All sprites had healing powers, a power that Fae had not been gifted with.

The most she could manage in terms of healing was cauterizing wounds with her ice until they got someone injured to a sprite. Therefore many towns and villages had sprites living there to act as healers for the sick and wounded.

They also had prophetic powers. Many of the sprites spoke in riddles or complete nonsense that she had made a game of trying to figure out as a child. She would head to the medical wing of the castle to chat with Kika and try to figure out exactly what she was telling her.

There were Fae that could actually piece together the jumbled wisdom from the sprites, making them invaluable as well. They could essentially be the conduits for the sprites and ultimately tell the future. She had never once figured out a vision Kika had tried to tell her.

The Winter sprites from her home were angelic creatures. They were small enough to fit in your palm, with shimmering white membranous wings. They would flitter around your head to spew their jargon and riddles incessantly. Their skin was the colour of glittering opals that reflected the sun in a bedazzling kaleidoscope of colours whenever they went outside. Each sprite wore their own spectacular outfit made of petals and leaves that they would make themselves, like rose petal skirts and bonnets from buttercups.

Maewyn had absolutely adored them. One time, she had even tried to make herself a skirt just like Kika's but had failed spectacularly. At the time, she had no knowledge of how to sew, so she had tried to weld the flower petals together with ice. The result was a skirt so heavy, she could barely lift it off the ground to even put it on, and when she did finally lift it up, she dropped it, and it shattered, leaving frozen petals and ice scattered across her bedroom floor.

The fire sprites before her now were the complete opposite of the sprites she grew up with, in every way. They were various hues of orange and red, with hair of flames to match. They still wore various outfits made of natural objects, but instead of flowers, they wore dresses made from pine cone scales and hats from acorn tops. They were glorious shades of ombre that cast a faint glow across the snowy ground around them.

What was the most concerning about them, however, was how cold they looked despite being huddled around the fires. They were shivering and huddled close together to keep their heat from dissipating on the wind.

One particularly bold sprite dusted off the fine layer of snow from her shoulders and flew up to them hesitantly. She stopped right in front of Maewyn, her black eyes a mixture of confusion and wonder.

"It's the Flaming Ice," she whispered in awe, and all the little sprites around the clearing looked up, locking eyes with Maewyn.

The way they looked at her wasn't malicious, and she felt no need to raise her weapons against them, but it unsettled her all the same. What in the world did they mean by the flaming ice? Had they seen something about her in their visions?

"I'm sorry... the what?" she asked, knowing full well the sprite probably wouldn't clarify.

"The one who is the ticket to the gate. The one who both reverses time and is the catalyst for the future."

The statement made no sense to her at all and based on the looks on Novak's and Rory's faces, it didn't make sense to them either.

Rory shrugged.

She tried again. "Can you tell me what happened here?"

She tried to speak as softly as possible. The little sprite wasn't afraid, but she certainly looked a bit dishevelled. Her acorn hat was askew, her dress was covered in frost, and shivers raked her body every few seconds.

"The man who calls himself the king of everything, but is the ruler of nothing, took his revenge," she explained to Maewyn in a tiny voice. "His goal was to weaken the fire."

She tried to figure out precisely what the small sprite was telling her.

Someone had taken revenge on them? And trapped them here, maybe? They certainly didn't look like they wanted to be here.

She couldn't imagine fire sprites would choose to live here. The more she looked around, the more she realized how desolate the place was.

There was evidence that the sprites had been here for some time, and she was amazed that they could survive up here at all. Fire sprites lived for the heat and warmth.

"Are you trapped here?" She tried to clarify.

The little sprite pointed towards the fog and then down the path in the direction they were headed. "The fog is hungry, and home is blocked. We have dwelled here for the entirety of some lifetimes."

Hmm yeah, that definitely sounds like they are trapped here, she thought.

"Why is the way blocked? I assume you all used to live in the Molten Court?"

"The wind put the half-bird, half-man there." The little fire sprite glanced over her shoulder again, fear in her eyes.

Maewyn again tried to decipher what she was saying, but her brain was feeling muddled and overrun with the statements. She groaned inwardly at the thought of carrying on this conversation for much longer.

Novak interrupted, though, solving the riddle for her. "A harpy. There's a harpy blocking the path back to the Molten Court."

The little sprite nodded solemnly and beckoned them to follow her. She brought them to the closest fire and gestured for them to sit down around it. It was a nice gesture, but the small flames did little to even warm their toes.

"The half n' half won't let the sprites return. And the fog is always hungry. Much too dangerous." She shivered and held her tiny hands to the fire.

Maewyn had a strong urge to hold the sprite in her hands to try and warm her up but wasn't sure how she would react.

This poor creature.

Trapped up here in a world of ice and snow for who knows how long. What kind of person would want to do that? Why would they want to take away the Molten Court's sprites?

"What is your name?" Maewyn asked.

"I am Iliada."

"Well, Iliada, what would you say about us getting rid of the... er... half and half for you?"

The sprite nodded, but Maewyn had a feeling she already knew they would be coming to their aid long before they even set foot into the mountains. The offer to help came as no surprise to her or her fellow sprites.

"The spirits of the fallen ones are indebted," she replied and glanced over at a small mound behind her.

Curious, Maewyn rose from her crouched position by the fire to take a look. The small pile was covered with snow but rose a few inches up off the ground.

She bent down to brush some of the snow away, only to see small hands poking up from the mound.

She brushed more snow away to reveal the bodies of *hundreds* of fire sprites. Their eyes were frozen and unseeing, and their little fingers were brittle and frozen. Horror flooded through her, and she stumbled backwards.

Hundreds of them had died up here.

How many sprites had been led up here and subsequently trapped? Thousands? Of which there were now only hundreds?

Her heart ached at the loss these small beings must have endured, trapped in the snowy mountains, struggling every day to survive the brutal storms that swept through. The small amount of heat they produced did nothing to counteract blizzards and avalanches. They had lived through so much more than she had in her entire lifetime.

One harpy. That was all they had to stop.

That couldn't be that hard… right?

CHAPTER 23

ASH

"Adelia? Where did you go?" Ash called.

He rose from setting his cloak on the dusty ground, brushing it off for good measure. It certainly wasn't how he expected to be spending the night, but he couldn't help feeling a little flicker of excitement knowing he would get to fall asleep next to Adelia tonight.

Surely, she wouldn't be stubborn enough to deny him keeping her warm for the night, right?

He looked over his shoulder and saw her bending over the lake.

What the...

Then she cupped her hands and slurped up the water like they had stumbled upon an oasis.

Oh no. No, no, no.

"Adelia!"

Forgetting the cloak, he sprinted over to her as she stood up and began to lift her shirt over her head, stumbling towards the lake.

Shit!

Running over, he watched as she flung her shirt into the water, grinning from ear to ear. The shirt landed in the inky lake, where it soaked up the black water and sank to the bottom. She was never getting that back, that's for sure.

He had absolutely no idea what was going on in her head right now, but he did know one thing—that water was dangerous. And if she got in, she'd never climb out.

Ash reached her and snagged her hands before she managed to strip off any other clothing, and she looked at him in bewilderment.

"Are you coming swimming with me?" she asked him innocently.

"No! You can't go swimming, Adelia!" It was a true testament to his willpower that he kept his eyes from drifting down.

She furrowed her eyebrows. "Why not?"

"That water is dangerous. It will *kill* you."

She laughed. "No, it won't!"

She looked at the lake over her shoulder lovingly. "It calls to me. Can't you hear it?" she whispered.

She looked back toward him and seemed to notice him for the first time. Her glassy eyes roved over his body and her pupils dilated.

"You're beautiful," she whispered in awe and reached out her fingers to touch his chest. She grazed them across his pecs and down his abs. He sucked in a breath.

She took a tentative step closer and moved to lift his shirt over the top of his head.

He couldn't help but laugh. "If you wanted my clothes off so badly, you could have just asked, but now you're drunk."

He grabbed her hands to stop her from stripping him down. "Come on, let's sit over there for a bit."

Ash pointed to the cloak he set down on the ground.

"Why?"

"I have something to show you over there. Will you follow me?"

Fuck. How am I going to keep her from jumping into that lake?

Surprisingly, she nodded and laced her fingers with his. He led her towards the boulders and sat her down, doing his best to keep his eyes level with hers. Because sitting in front of a semi-naked Adelia did more to him than he cared to admit. He sat directly in front of her, pinning her between the wall, the boulders, and him. It would have to do.

She lasted a whole thirty seconds before she remembered the water again.

"Please, please, let's go swimming." Her voice cracked with emotion, and tears filled her hazy eyes as he denied her the only thing in life she was convinced she needed.

"Adelia, we can't. It's dangerous." He could keep telling her, but it was evident she couldn't comprehend it.

The only cure was time.

"How can you deny me the only thing in life that will make me happy?" She was growing angry now.

He sighed. The water she drank was running havoc on her emotions.

"You're so cruel! All you want to do is cause me pain!" Her spittle flew at him, but he merely wiped it from his face and concentrated on blocking her path to the lake.

This goddamned lake.

"You're a monster!" she screamed.

If only she knew how true that actually was.

Luckily, she zoned out again before he could reply. Her eyes glazed over as she stared at the lake like a forlorn lover at her unrequited love.

He thought they had made it very clear from the start to stay alert and that the caves were dangerous. Maybe he had underestimated how thirsty she was and that in her exhaustion, she hadn't been able to resist the lure of the magical waters.

He should have been more specific about the dangers in this cave, but it had been a long time since he had travelled through here, and he hadn't been able to remember the exact effects of the water. All he remembered was that the caverns were dangerous, and when he had travelled through with his dad, his dad had never let go of his hand. He had been so young at the time.

"Who are you?" she blurted out, having returned to staring at him.

She doesn't even remember me?

Adelia reached out with her fingers, eyes glassy and unfocused again as she brushed his hair back from his face. Her stare was so intense, it felt like she was staring through to his soul. It broke him to see her looking at him like that and know it was only because of the water.

"I feel like I've seen you in my dreams," she whispered in awe. "Dreams where you're running your hands down my body and trailing kisses in their wake. I remember feeling like I would combust from your touch alone. I want to feel like that again." She moved her hands lower this time and tried to unbuckle his pants.

Ash threw his head back in frustration. "Adelia, what are you *doing* to me?"

Any other time, he would have loved this. But seeing her like this was something he never wanted to experience. She was a slave to the magic of the water, not in her right state.

He closed his eyes to steady his pulse and took a deep breath.

Then Adelia bolted.

She jumped up and tried to dart past him while he was distracted.

Damn it!

He lunged at her, tackling her to the ground before she had a chance to get to the lake.

She wriggled and squirmed beneath him, but luckily he was stronger. Ash held her until she calmed again, and she rolled to face him.

"Are you calmer now?" he asked her exasperatedly.

She nodded, even though he knew she still had no idea what was going on.

"I'm going to get up now. Please don't bolt again, ok?"

But she shook her head.

"No? What do you mean no?"

Then Adelia leaned forward and pressed her lips to his exposed neck.

The kiss was featherlight and soft, just a whisper of breath against his neck.

His pulse jumped at the contact and he couldn't help but close his eyes as she trailed kisses down to his collarbone.

He really shouldn't give into this…

Without meaning to, he loosened his grip on her hands and she brought them up to pull him closer. She nipped at his neck playfully, and he growled in response. He ground his hips into her, unable to stop himself. She whimpered in response.

What was she *doing* to him? He needed to get it together.

This wasn't Adelia.

He wanted nothing more than for her to look at him like this, to touch him like this.

But he wanted her to mean it.

Her eyes were glazed over, unseeing and unaware of anything she did or said.

Ash pulled away, ignoring the throbbing below his waist. He

grabbed her and pulled her to her feet. He led her silently back to the corner. He forcefully sat her down again and resumed his spot, blocking her path to the lake.

He sighed.

It was going to be a very long night.

CHAPTER 24

MAEWYN

Maewyn, Rory, and Novak proceeded through the makeshift camp of the fire sprites to the looming mountain pass beyond. Maewyn braced her knees with each step down the slope to avoid picking up speed on the decline. As they went down, the walls of the crevasse around them rose higher and higher. The mountains stretched up on either side of them until the sky above was a thin sliver of blue.

The snowy walls of the pass were ragged and unstable; bits of rock would break off and come tumbling down towards the path below. The path itself was no more than a few metres wide, and they had to veer into a single file line.

Maewyn kept glancing up at the sky, expecting a dark shape to blot out the light above them. She knew harpies were large, vicious creatures. They were the physical embodiment of wind and darkness.

Her mother had told her stories about how they would snatch Fae who dared to wander the mountains alone. They would keep them trapped high in mountain caves that one could only access with wings. Harpies were intelligent beings, and it was said they grew tired of living solitary lives. They would keep Fae captives in their frostbitten caves for as long as possible before they succumbed to hypothermia or starvation. Then the harpy would search for a new companion to warm their lonely caves.

She shivered at the thought. She could stand the cold weather longer than most, but even she wasn't immune to it completely. Through the sliver of sky above them, the mountain peaks appeared like flecks in the distance. It would be bone-chillingly cold up there, and the lack of oxygen could kill a Fae quickly. Fae weren't invincible, they just lived longer than humans. The average Fae could live for hundreds of years if given the chance.

The farther they got from the fire sprites, the more she wished they had convinced some of them to come with them. She knew together the three of them were strong, but Ash's and Adelia's absences weighed heavy on her heart.

Novak, Rory, and Ash each held a piece of her, and for the first time in years, they had been separated. Splitting up had been unavoidable, but she felt incomplete, like she was missing a vital organ or was stripped of her magic. She hadn't felt this way since Dax left the group. It had taken them so long to find a new rhythm with only four of them, but now it felt off-kilter again.

She glanced down at the arctic fox trotting beside her. He glanced up to meet her eyes, and she knew he felt it too. Yes, they were strong as three, but not as strong as they would be with Ash. He fought with fire and fury and was the type of person you wanted to have at your back in a fight. He'd sacrifice himself before letting any of them get hurt. He told them it was because he had more healing knowledge and could take care of himself. He knew how to use herbs and sew up wounds better than the rest of them.

It was refreshing to see him opening up since Adelia had joined them. He was having a hard time keeping a straight face when Adelia was around, and she saw the way he stole glances at her when he didn't think anyone was watching.

Maewyn wasn't surprised, though. Adelia was brave and spunky, and frankly, she loved being around her.

She wished Adelia could stay with them forever. Maewyn glanced at Novak, their fearless leader, with guilt. Novak wasn't the type of girl you'd giggle and laugh with. She was everything they needed in a Faerie Guard leader, but Maewyn hadn't realized the type of friendship she was missing until Adelia had walked into her life.

They could chat for hours and she could see herself only growing closer with Adelia. And after Dax, they needed a new Wind Fae on the team anyway. She wondered what would happen when they found Teilio. Would Adelia go back to the human world?

She selfishly hoped not.

Adelia fit so seamlessly into their little family. It would be a shame to deny that. She vowed to make sure to tell her that, and she hoped Ash had the balls to tell her as well. He may be able to fight off a banshee or wyvern, but he was useless when it came to opening up.

Ash had been a part of their team for years and hadn't once talked about his past. She knew nothing of his family or life before being a Faerie Guard. She didn't even know why he wore those gloves like a second skin.

When they first met him, she had pestered him about it, but he only seemed to close himself off more every time she asked. So eventually, she stopped. She knew Ash had a lot of demons and suspected his childhood had been scarring. He was clearly still trying to deal with it himself and hadn't realized opening up about it might help bring him closure. But she'd be here when he was ready. It really didn't matter to her now anyway. He was basically family. If he wanted his space on those topics, she'd give it to him. He had never given her any reason to distrust him.

Lost in her thoughts but still aware of her surroundings, Maewyn noticed a flash of black in her periphery. She halted Novak and Rory, following suit, and looked up at a snowy rock shelf halfway up the cliff wall.

"Did you see that?" she whispered cautiously.

Novak nodded. "It was likely put here to stop the sprites from returning to their court. We might not know why, but we are freeing them today. They have suffered long enough."

"Agreed," Rory said.

Up on the shelf above them sat what could only be the harpy.

It was a creature from the darkest corners of your dreams. Its body was encased in shadowy tendrils that cascaded down the mountain like black fingers. They ebbed and flowed around its body like a living, breathing entity. Beneath the shadows, Maewyn could barely make out a face, with piercing golden eyes that locked with hers. Its eyes screamed with both malice and sadness. There was a hungry desire for violence but also a conflicting need for something more. Could it be the loneliness she had been told about in fables? She couldn't imagine having shadows like that enveloping you, scaring away every other living creature. Then, the shadows pulsed outwards, and the creature's eyes flashed in anger as it realized they weren't merely passing through.

The three of them had stopped and drawn their weapons, the cold metal against the scabbards echoing through the crevasse. This creature knew they were here to kill it. Maewyn did nothing to hide the truth in her eyes as she held the creature's gaze.

The creature spread its wings and dove off the cliff before them. As it drew closer, there was power in each stroke of its giant wings and its deadly talons that glinted against the white snow. The combination of a human face and head with the wings and body of a bird was revolting. It looked like both creatures had been torn in two and sewn back together like a science experiment gone wrong.

Closer and closer it dove, picking up speed as it approached them. There was nowhere to hide. They were trapped in the mountain pass with no cover other than a few fallen boulders. It certainly wasn't to their advantage.

But she was powerful here.

More powerful than anywhere else in Faerie, other than the Snow Court.

The snow and ice that surrounded them fed her powers, and she could feel the threads dangling in the air, calling to her.

She reached out to the magic around her, feeling each snowflake on the ground and each atom of water that had turned to ice.

She coaxed them to come to her call.

The harpy might be wind and darkness, but she was ice and light.

The harpy's darkness was inarguably menacing. It followed in trails as it flew closer, but her snow and ice were deceiving. The snow was endless. It could carpet the world with deceiving beauty. It was cold and unforgiving.

One snowflake was fragile and could melt at first touch, but together?

Together they were a blizzard that could steal your senses, rendering you blind and immobile.

People looked at her and underestimated her, but they had no idea of the power of frost. Snow lived for an eternity in the mountains, encasing the world in an endless cold.

She had access to an army. Each tiny snowflake was hers, and when they stuck together, she was unstoppable.

She smiled, and the blizzard began.

It swirled around the harpy with terrifying ferocity, whitening out their location. The three of them scattered, darting out in different directions to confuse the creature.

It bellowed in rage, a mix between a scream and a bird cry. It shattered the mountain's silence, and Maewyn covered her ears frantically. The harpy wouldn't be able to see them down here, but that meant they also couldn't track it.

She waited a few seconds, hoping it was enough time for Rory and Novak to take to the walls for cover.

She took the risk and lifted the blizzard, ready to attack... but the harpy was gone.

She had expected it to be disoriented in the snow, and when she looked at Rory, he was just as confused.

It had vanished.

She sat with bated breath for one second. Two seconds. Three.

And then it appeared.

It had taken to the skies and was barrelling down towards them in a nosedive, faster than before.

Rory dove left to narrowly avoid the harpy's talons and Maewyn reached for her power again. From the wall of the cavern, she created icicles that shot out horizontally towards the harpy.

But the harpy was agile. It missed getting impaled and dove down again. Maewyn took a chance and stretched the ice across the top of the cavern to create a barrier across the top of the pass.

It trapped the harpy down here with them. It was a risk, but she was worried the harpy would take to the skies again, and it seemed most dangerous at high speeds. With only a limited area down here, it would have to rely on pure strength.

It bellowed again, its cry so piercing that some of the ice barrier shattered, and tiny shards rained down on them.

But the barrier held.

The harpy floated above them as if unsure who to attack first, but Rory didn't give it a chance to think. He sprinted to the wall of the crevasse and planted his foot on it. He used his momentum to launch himself into the air and soared upwards like an eagle. Time froze as Maewyn watched him float through the air and swing his sword around in a giant sweeping arc towards the harpy. His sword sliced through the thick, black aura and connected with the harpy's legs. Black blood spewed onto the snowy ground like an inkblot.

Forced into action, the harpy reached out with its talons towards Rory as he landed on the soft powder and sank them into his left shoulder.

His screams matched the harpy's from before, and Novak and Maewyn raced towards him.

Both she and Novak accosted the creature with ice and water. Maewyn tried to impale its wings, and Novak attempted to disorient it by concentrating her water in its face.

But the creature was too fast.

Every time they directed an attack at it, it darted away with its mighty wings. It evaded each attack with ease.

It was a game of cat and mouse, and Maewyn was slowly becoming winded. She had barely landed any blows as they chased the creature around the pass, trying to pin it down.

She was breathing heavily, but, despite all the effort, they had yet to gain an advantage.

She had to figure something out quickly.

Rory's shoulder was congealed with blood. Each second the

harpy evaded them, he drew closer to losing consciousness. The concussion and now this? He wouldn't last much longer.

He tried to stay upright, but the unsteadiness in his stance was visible.

Just then, faint orange lights came down the passageway from the sprite camp.

What were the sprites doing?

"Get out of here!" she bellowed. "It's too dangerous! Get back to your camp!"

But they kept coming. The tiny sprites flooded the area, holding little sticks and pebbles like weapons.

Maewyn caught Iliada's gaze, and the little sprite nodded in solidarity.

The sprites took to the air, whizzing around the harpy like tiny meteors. They darted in and out of the harpy's black aura, some stabbing it with sticks and others pressing their tiny burning hands to its wings when an opening presented itself.

Maewyn watched in awe as the fearless sprites took their freedom into their own hands. They managed to damage the harpy's wings enough that it came tumbling from the sky.

As it spiralled to the ground, it twisted and turned its talon's, slashing out in anger at anything that came close. Maewyn watched frozen, while sprite after sprite was wiped from the sky or impaled on its talons.

A few sprites were knocked back by its powerful wings into the walls of the crevasse, and Maewyn knew their little bodies would never survive a blow like that.

They fell, and Maewyn watched as their lights dimmed. They faded from fiery orange to faint yellow against the white snow.

As soon as the harpy hit the ground, ice formed into a sword of piercing cold and unforgiving resilience in Maewyn's palm. She stepped into the black tendrils surrounding the harpy.

Her vision was partially obscured, but she could see the beast well enough to know where to hit.

She brought the sword down onto the harpy's chest with a feral scream.

It thrashed out with its talons again, narrowly missing her, but she pushed the sword in farther. It slid between the harpy's feathers and into its rib cage before piercing the soft organ beneath.

Its dying screams were swept away with the wind, and the darkness surrounding it evaporated like mist.

All that was left was the grotesque half-bird, half-human with sad, unseeing eyes.

Then the sprites' cheers grew around her. The little beings embraced one another, little orange tears streaking down their delicate features.

She wanted to join in, but she felt hollow and empty.

All around them lay the bodies of countless brave sprites who sacrificed themselves to save their friends and family.

She bent down and picked up a small boy, who was only the size of her thumb, out of the cold snow. His eyes were closed, and he looked almost peaceful.

But her world was far from peaceful. She focused on taking deep breaths and calming her thunderous heart. It was a challenge to stop the tears welling up in her eyes.

The mood called for rain. The sky should be dark and ominous, but instead, light flurries fell from fluffy clouds that had rolled in.

Snowflakes stuck to the boy's eyelashes and hair, giving him an angelic look. He was so young. He had a whole lifetime ahead of him.

In this world of snow and ice, they had lost many great warriors.

Because that's what these sprites were.

Warriors.

The world around her was slowly covered in a soft blanket of white, while they worked to remove the bodies of the fallen sprites from the powder.

She carefully placed each one in the pockets of her cloak, silently thanking them and wishing them safe passage to the beyond.

AFTER COLLECTING ALL the bodies of the fallen sprites, they found their way back to the camp where the sprites had made their home. They all took their time burying the bodies and saying goodbyes.

Iliada, looking forlorn but grateful, came over to land in Maewyn's hand. "We are forever in your debt. We can return to our homeland now."

Maewyn smiled at the little sprite. "Would you like to accompany us? We are headed to the Molten Court ourselves."

But the sprite shook her head. "We may not have much, but we need to pack our belongings and say goodbye to our home. Many young sprites have only known this mountain as home. It will be quite the shock for them to return to our homeland."

"Ok. Well, safe travels. I hope we meet again one day."

"Safe travels, Flaming Ice. The future will hold many trials for you. Do not let it thaw you. Your ice is your equalizer."

Maewyn just shook her head, content to be mystified with Iliada's riddles. After today, she didn't have the energy to try and solve them.

CHAPTER 25

The world refocused as Adelia emerged from her stupor. As if waking up from a medical procedure, her thoughts were addled, her movements heavy and sluggish.

She tried to blink the sticky sleep dust from her eyes, and the blue-green light of the cavern came into focus. She realized she was slumped over a boulder, and Ash's cloak had been draped over her. She groaned and tried to move, only to notice that under the cloak, she had only her bra on.

Adelia squealed and pulled the cloak tighter around her body.

Ash had been dozing off right in front of her, their faces so close, she could feel his even breath against her cheek.

He blinked awake at her sudden movement and looked at her cautiously. "Adelia…?" he asked hesitantly.

It sounded like he was afraid. But why would he be afraid of her?

What had even happened? The last thing she remembered was taking a drink from the lake…

Oh, God, I drank from the lake.

She remembered the pull of the lake, the magnetic attraction. How it had muddled her thoughts and compelled her to take a drink.

How in the world had that even happened?

What had she been thinking?

She should have known better.

She pulled the cloak tighter around herself. "What… what happened?" She was almost afraid to ask.

At her response, Ash's features visibly softened with relief. "Oh, thank the Orb, you're back." He gave her his signature smirk and eyebrow quirk. "As for what happened, I don't think you want to know." He chuckled darkly.

Dread coiled in her stomach.

"Where is my shirt, Ash?"

His eyes darkened. "I didn't touch you. I promise."

And she believed him. But did he look? Did he notice the key hanging from her necklace? Panic seized her chest, but Ash was acting normally. He wasn't showing any indication of noticing the very key they were searching for was hanging from her neck.

But he continued. "You didn't hold yourself to the same promise, though, that's for sure."

Oh God.

Heat crept up her neck. He was definitely right. She wasn't sure she would ever want to know what she had done while under the influence of that magical water.

"Promise me you'll never speak of this again?"

He smirked. "Cross my heart." And he mimed an X over his heart.

He stood gingerly and glanced down at his black and gold cloak draped over her. "Keep it. We need to get moving. I don't want to spend another moment in this cursed cavern."

Adelia had to agree.

She put his cloak on properly, doing up all the breast buttons to secure it tightly around her chest. It smelled of him, like campfire smores and the forest floor. It was thick, sturdy leather, and even though it was too big, it held its shape around her shoulders.

"I need a few minutes before we leave." She hesitated for a second before continuing, "Do you think the water is safe to wash with? I'd like to clean my stump and let it breathe for a bit. Here, take my sock and dunk it maybe? I can wash with that and we don't have to stay near the water?"

Ash nodded. "Good idea. Wait here."

Adelia watched as he carefully made his way over to the lake, dipped her sock in, letting it soak up as much as possible, and then brought it back over. She then took the next few minutes to clean and let it dry.

After she was done and her prosthetic was back on, Ash reached down to help her to her feet, the matching leather of his gloves scraping roughly on her palm. "Come on, let's go join our friends." Her heart hiccupped at the statement.

Were they her friends? She still wasn't sure. She took one last look at the glowing cavern, branding the memory of its deceiving beauty in her mind. It was a reminder of the dangers Faerie had in store for her and to stay alert when they arrived at the Molten Court.

"We should make it out of the tunnel by this afternoon," Ash announced. She knew he was hoping at the end they would find Novak, Rory, and Maewyn waiting for them—safe and uninjured.

"Please tell me the rest of the way there is just plain, old tunnels. No surprises."

"Well…"

Adelia balked at him, but he laughed. "I'm kidding! The rest are boring, old tunnels, I promise. You'll have to deal with me keeping you entertained for the rest of the way."

"Oh joy. You've been so much fun to spend time with," she mumbled, only half-joking.

He leaned into her and bumped her with his shoulder playfully. Without his cloak, he looked more casual than she had ever seen him. His cotton long-sleeved shirt hung loosely around his collar, and he walked with more ease than before.

"Tell me about what it was like to grow up in the Wind Court."

"Ahh, you want me to tell you about all the different birds I've seen, don't you?"

She laughed dryly. "You aren't a birdwatcher, so I'm not sure I trust your identification skills. You'd probably try and convince me you've seen an ivory-billed woodpecker."

"Don't tell me you *haven't* seen an ivory-billed woodpecker?" he asked her, looking scandalized.

She rolled her eyes, and Ash glanced up at the cave's ceiling mournfully. "Ah, yes, they are very rare. Purple heads, green bodies, and blue legs. With a pink bill twice its size."

She laughed. "You're not even close!"

He shrugged in defeat. "You got me. I spent all my time learning about plants actually."

"Plants?"

"Yes, plants and their healing properties. I can make a mean tonic to settle the stomach and a paste to remove scars."

Adelia looked at him incredulously. "You can't remove scars with a paste."

"You forget you are in Faerie, Adelia. Expect the unexpected."

"Okay, fine. Why healing?"

"It calmed me when I was treating people. It felt good to do something good. You know, help people."

"Who knew you were actually a softie at heart, Ash... wait, Ash what? Do you have a last name?"

"Nope. Just Ash."

"Well, *just Ash*. You continue to surprise me."

"You don't even know the half of it," he replied dryly.

Adelia couldn't help but wonder what other surprises he had in store for her, but she was excited to find out.

Curiosity glimmered in his eyes. "Can I ask you something? Only if you feel comfortable talking about it."

She nodded, pretty sure she knew where this was going.

"Can you tell me about your leg? You were so adamant about hiding it at first, but something obviously changed."

She glanced down at her prosthetic with a mixture of both gratitude and loss.

"It happened when I was a teenager. I was sick." She didn't tell the whole story very often. Most people didn't ask.

"I was diagnosed with a rare form of cancer. Called a synovial sarcoma. It's a tumor that grows in the soft tissue. Mine just happened to grow in my leg around the nerves and blood vessels. So they had to amputate my leg. They did it to save my life and I'll be forever grateful that it worked and I'm standing here alive today. But waking up and not having a leg anymore was something that took me a long time to come to terms with. I had a lot of self-esteem issues. My whole body image changed and it took a lot of work to come to terms with that and learn how to accept myself again. I guess when I came here, all that came rushing back. I was afraid of judgement and scared to be myself." Adelia took a steadying breath.

"Oh, Adelia," Ash breathed. And she knew if she looked over, she wouldn't see pity, just sorrow that she had gone through so much at such a young age.

"I'm not going to pretend like it wasn't tough. I was so sick. And there was a point where they didn't know if I'd make it. But

I'm a fighter." She looked up to meet his gaze and smiled, only to find him looking at her with a sort of reverence.

Ash nodded. "Yes. You are."

"My dad was there for me through all of it. And I know he's my dad, so he had to be, but he helped me recover in more ways than one. I wouldn't be the woman I am today without him."

"He sounds like a wonderful man."

"He is." She tried to picture his sandy hair and the little wrinkles by his eyes. His worn hands from years of working in a kitchen.

"Well, thank you for telling me. You're a pretty amazing woman yourself, Adelia."

"I thought you didn't want me thinking you were a nice guy?"

He eyed her slyly. "Oh, I can be bad, don't worry."

Adelia laughed, purposely exaggerating her eye roll, but her heart was a little lighter knowing he knew her story.

CHAPTER 26

I t began as a small pinprick of light in the distance. It grew larger and larger until Adelia and Ash were standing at the gaping exit of the cave. Adelia blinked as she adjusted to the light.

After being underground for days, it was disorienting.

The scenery on this side of the mountain pass was more tropical than the other side. Lush ferns covered the grounds and rough vines stretched across the canopy. The air here was stuffier, either a product of the environment or an indication that they were closing in on the Molten Court.

Once her eyes adjusted, she spotted a small figure crashing through the underbrush towards her.

Maewyn.

"You guys are ok!" Maewyn wailed, relief visible in both her body language and voice as she collided with Adelia's chest.

Adelia hadn't realized how accustomed she had become to her presence, but she felt a tightness in her chest ease knowing they were all back together again.

It wasn't that she couldn't manage without them, but when

they were all together, it felt *right*. But in the same moment, the Molten Key pulsed with heat in reminder of her lies.

She was deceiving them.

She couldn't let herself forget that.

She figured Ash hadn't seen the key during the cave incident... she assumed he would have said something. Either she was incredibly lucky, or he was keeping her secret. She had to figure out if he knew somehow.

She couldn't shake the feeling that she should tell them she had the key. They probably liked her enough that they would follow through on the rescue mission whether she had the key or not.

But she wasn't sure.

To them, she was just a random girl, an end to their means. These feelings—of rightness, of belonging, of friendship—were likely one-sided.

Maewyn finally released her hold, and Adelia got a good look at her. She was definitely worse for wear than when they parted. Actually, she realized they were all pretty beat up. Rory had a makeshift bandage around his shoulder and a dazed look in his eyes. Novak was walking with a slight limp she was trying desperately to hide.

She wanted to ask what happened, but Novak's face told her enough. The mountain pass was as bad as they predicted. Even though her own travels through the cave had been eventful, clearly it had not been as hard as their journey.

Their trip through the caverns had been embarrassing rather than dangerous.

She had been dying to ask exactly what she had done while she was under the water's spell but was terrified of the answer. She'd probably never be able to look at him in the eyes again once he told her.

So she pretended like nothing had happened, despite still

wearing nothing but his cloak that came down well past her knees.

She was in a literal walk of shame outfit.

Not something she ever thought would happen in Faerie while on a mission to save her father. There was no doubt that the others had noticed this detail as well and had decided not to comment on it either.

They told the others a brief version of their travels through the cave, Ash leaving out the drama, and no one questioned him about it. Then Maewyn filled her and Ash in about the mountain pass, the sprites, and the harpy.

"Where are these sprites now?" she asked. The little creatures sounded adorable, and she looked around expectantly.

"They had to pack up their camp and then were headed back to the Molten Court. It's been a long time since they've seen their homeland, and they had no reason to wait for us, while we waited for you two."

Obviously, she didn't blame them, but the thought of seeing a little sprite in an acorn hat was almost too much to handle.

It was every fairy-tale bedtime story come true. She recalled playing outside in the backyard as a child, building little 'homes' for pixies and sprites with twigs and leaves.

Lost sprites will spend the night there, Adelia. If they are ever in need, they will have shelter, her dad used to tell her. Knowing what she did now, she realized her dad was not simply playing make-believe.

It made her wonder about encounters she had in the human realm and how many of them were actually magic. How when walking through the forest, sometimes you'd trip on nothing or get your hair caught on a branch you *swore* wasn't there before. How many of these little moments were lost sprites who had made their home in the human world and got a laugh out of teasing humans?

Novak interrupted her thoughts. "Now that we've had our happy little reunion, let's get back on the road." She turned and limped off without waiting for them, like she always did.

Adelia couldn't help but smile. Leave it to Novak to squash their reunion and get them back on track.

AFTER ANOTHER FEW hours of travel through the rainforest, Adelia finally caught sight of the Molten Court appearing on the horizon. The forest thinned out, until it was a measly few trees that shielded them from the court. A volcano consumed the sky high above the homes. It was ancient and monstrous, towering over the court like a malevolent god. She knew it to be the residence of Queen Karai. The castle had been carved into the volcano itself hundreds of years ago, with snaking pathways that ran alongside the lava inside.

It was a home made for a monster.

Smaller homes made of basalt littered the ground around it, as if they had risen from the lava. Compared to the castle, they were pitiful. It was evident the Fae that made their home in the Molten Court had not been well cared for over the past few years. But the sight didn't surprise Adelia. After what she had heard of Queen Karai, it came as no shock that she had kept the weaning resources to herself and left her people to starve and wither away.

There were steaming geysers, exploding periodically, spraying boiling water into the air with a resounding boom. Cobblestone roads wove around them, narrowly avoiding the spray. Grey ash settled over the ground, giving some areas the appearance of snow.

It's almost beautiful, Adelia thought. *In a desolate, macabre kind of way.*

Most breathtaking of all, though, was the moat of molten

lava that surrounded the entire court. It gurgled and sputtered as it crept slowly along, providing a deadly barrier between them and their destination. Every few moments, the magma would bubble up and explode like popcorn, flinging lava in all directions.

It was a bit like watching the fireworks on New Year's Eve. The bright lights stole your gaze away with a mesmerizing explosion of light and colour. Every year on New Year's, her dad hosted a neighbour backyard bash. He'd spend the day cooking appetizers, and then all the dads would launch fireworks from the cliff. Adelia would spend most of the night corralling the children and making sure they didn't fall off the cliff themselves. But she laughed now, thinking they would have ended up in Faerie alive and well if they had.

They all stood far enough back from the river so that any Molten beyond it wouldn't be able to pick them out from the waning trees of the Blacklore Woods.

Novak spoke in hushed tones. "Before the Molten War, The Basalt Bridge stood open all the time." She looked intently at where Adelia assumed the bridge once was. "The Molten were the most powerful Fae for centuries, as forest fires ravaged the earth in the drying climate. But Queen Karai and King Orodani of the Wind Court never met eye to eye. There's one rumour he tried to have her overthrown because he thought she was unfit to rule. Their squabble escalated and eventually led to the war you know about. The other courts stayed neutral despite their alliances with the Wind Court due to their fear of Queen Karai and her Molten army. I think they knew Queen Karai was in the wrong, especially for using forbidden magic, but they were too afraid to intervene."

She scanned the edge of the river again and continued, "The moat was originally used to keep Fae out who weren't welcome in the court—there was always a Molten Guard on the other side who would create the Basalt Bridge from the lava below for anyone who needed to cross it—like traders, guards, and royalty."

She stared into the distance like she could picture the grand entrance to the court still standing. "I remember it being spell-binding, watching the Keeper of the Bridge move the lava into the air, and then cool it into the shape of a bridge high above the river below. I only came to the court once, but I'll never forget the spectacle."

Adelia followed Novak's gaze to the east, where two guard towers stood looking down onto the river. She assumed the Keeper would create the bridge between the two guard towers.

But now?

There was nothing.

There was no safe way for them to cross the fiery river below, and no guards on the other side who would create the bridge for them to cross.

Novak's brilliant plan to get across required stealth appar-ently, and a whole lot of luck. She really wished now that she had been able to get a dragonfly to land on her when they were back in the cave.

All they could do was hope there were no Molten guarding the old bridge as they approached the towers. The other courts still had no idea the gate was fully down, so they had no reason to stand guard.

"So where is the gate?" she whispered to Rory beside her.

"The gate isn't an *actual* gate, Adelia."

Oh.

"Wait, what? How?"

"We live in a world of magic. Think of the gate as more of a barrier Teilio created with his magic. A barrier around the entire moat to keep the Molten inside."

Right.

"Well, silly me, how could I not realize," she harrumphed back.

She looked for any tell-tale signs of the barrier, like the faint glimmer of light. She reached out her hand and met no resistance in the air before her.

This gate truly was down.

Novak looked at each of them sincerely. "All right, team. This is it. We get in, we get Teilio, and we get out." She looked around at her team fiercely.

"Our strength," she started.

"Our power," Maewyn replied.

"Our determination," Rory said with a small smile.

"Our allegiance," Ash finished.

They all looked at each other, much more than just determination in their eyes. Their faces shone with faith and resilience. The faces of four individuals, who were a family.

"Only together are we whole," they all finished together, leaving Adelia feeling unsure if the proclamation made her feel more secure... or less.

RORY BEGAN to carve out a section of the earth from in front of them about ten feet across and ten feet wide. The slab floated as if it were on strings down to the river and landed in the boiling lava with a soft splash. Novak wasted no time jumping down onto the raft. Her arms were out to balance her weight as it shifted, the raft threatening to toss her into the river.

Adelia looked incredulously at her. "*This* was your brilliant plan to get across the river?"

Ash snickered beside her and she went to glare at him, but he moved forward quickly to join Novak.

Why were these Fae always so eager to engage in life-threatening activities? Jumping off cliffs, rafting across molten lava rivers. What was next? Scaling the volcano free solo? Before coming here, the craziest thing she had ever tried was surfing as a kid. *Try* being the keyword. She had been tossed from the board within seconds, colliding with a jellyfish floating aimlessly through the water beside her.

And that had been it.

The faint scars on her flank served as a reminder of the failure, and she had been too scared to ever try again. That and she didn't want to spend thousands buying a surfing specific prosthetic, even though they looked super cool.

With a sigh, she hurried to join them before the slow current took the raft away from the edge, leaving her behind. As she jumped on, she stumbled. The raft lurched aggressively, and she fell into Ash.

He caught her with two strong hands, righting her before she took them all into the river with her.

Concern marred his features. "Are you all right?"

"I'm fine. Making the disabled girl jump onto a moving raft really wasn't a great idea, though," she said, pulling away despite every muscle that sang at her to move closer instead. His hands lingered on her a moment longer than necessary.

"Ok, Adelia, you're up. Give us a boost to the other side," Novak said just loudly enough to hear above the roar of the river.

This was what Rory had been training her for.

They needed her wind powers as much as they needed Rory's terrain, Maewyn's ice, and Novak's water. This was her chance to prove to them that they hadn't made a mistake in bringing her along.

She started by sitting down on the raft. She knew her limits, and balancing with her eyes closed was not one of them. Once she was, she closed her eyes like she had been instructed. It was slowly getting easier to feel the magic in the air as Ash had first described to her. When she focused enough, it was like she was in a snow globe that had been shaken up. The magic was like glitter falling gracefully around her and it felt like she could reach out and touch the soft flakes as they whirled around her.

She pulled as much wind magic as she could muster and tried to direct it out behind the boat.

A faint breeze resulted from the effort and mildly tousled her hair around.

Panicked, she looked at Rory. Despite using concentration to keep the raft together, he looked at her with utter confidence.

The look in his eyes spoke a thousand words, and Adelia was slowly beginning to understand why he didn't need to say what he was thinking all the time. He wore his emotions on his features, and there was no question he believed in her. It made her heart swell, and she found it comforting to think that a boy who was once a stranger could have so much trust in her already.

He knew she could do this.

She had to believe it too.

Trying again, she reached outward and this time a stronger wind picked up, sending the raft gliding slowly forward through the thick river. She now understood why Rory had looked so strained while they were back in the Blacklore Woods and he had held the dirt up to keep them hidden. Keeping the wind constant at their backs was much more difficult than creating a single gust.

She tried to keep it up to reach the other side as quickly as possible, to reduce the chance of being seen.

When they hit the other side, Novak grabbed it to steady the boat. Adelia slumped, exhausted from the effort, and found herself in someone's arms again. She knew without looking that it was Ash.

"Looks like *someone* has been practicing," he whispered into her ear.

"No thanks to you," she huffed back.

Just because they had gone through an ordeal in the caverns together didn't mean she forgave him for his cold behaviour from before. He had refused to help her with her magic back at the Wind Court and acted like she was the last person he wanted to speak to. He acted like he hadn't taken her to The Perch in the first place. And then she had to pretend they hadn't shared a moment up there.

"You still owe me an apology," she scoffed, trying to stand up, but he tightened his grip around her. In one fell swoop, he had her cradled in his arms.

"I saw you trying to get onto that ostrich earlier. There's no way I'm trusting you to get off this boat. *Especially* after using that much magic."

He leapt gracefully off the raft onto the solid ground, his powerful arms holding her close to his chest. His comforting smell of firewood wafted around her and muddled her thoughts.

"And for what it's worth, I'm sorry. I was acting childish. I... I..." He seemed to hesitate before continuing, like he wanted to say more. "I thought maybe if you didn't learn magic, you wouldn't come with us. It being dangerous and all."

She huffed again. "*You* don't get to make that decision for me. And I am more than capable of taking care of myself."

He set her down gently on her feet, taking extra time to brush imaginary dust off her shoulders as if he didn't want to let her go quite yet. He looked as if he wanted to say more, but Adelia quickly stepped away to follow the rest of the group heading towards the castle.

She felt so conflicted.

Her pulse jumped when he was near, and his closeness was comforting.

It was the feel of his arms around her and his steady feet beneath them.

He was a tether holding her down when she threatened to float into space. He kept her grounded in reality. He had enveloped her in a sense of security since jumping blindly off that cliff into this new world.

She felt safe when she was in his arms.

But that did not give him the right to assume she needed to be protected.

Wanting a man's closeness wasn't equivalent to *needing* it.

She had made, and would continue to make, her own decisions.

It didn't make sense why he wanted to protect her, anyway. Based on his fearful eyes at any mention of the Molten Court, she had begun to wonder if maybe there was something here they would need to protect *him* from.

Now that they were on the other side of their first obstacle, the group crept through the dark and empty streets of the Molten Court towards the volcano. The castle was carved into the volcano itself and it had dangerous-looking spires that clawed the stormy skies all around it. Thousands of bats flew in dizzying circles around the castle, darting in and out of windows. Light streamed out from a few of these windows and balconies high above. It gave the castle an illusion of warmth and kindness.

The darkness of the night around them, however, was not kind. It whispered it's dark promises to them, pressing in on them like an unwelcome, warm embrace.

It was disconcerting.

Adelia grew up with a thousand twinkling stars that greeted her every night. They would wink down at her, reminding her that even on her darkest nights, she could look up at them and be reminded that there was still light in the world.

But this sky was starless.

The dust clouds that rolled across the dark velvet sky obscured any trace of warm light, and despite the warmth from the volcano, Adelia felt nothing but cold.

The cold seeped deep in her bones, dread building with each step towards her father. She desperately wanted to succeed but was afraid of what the castle would bring. She had done ok on the raft, but did she have enough energy for the rest of the plan?

Before she had time to consider, they were at the castle and this time, there were guards.

They stood high above them on terraces around the volcano, peering down on the homes below like they were ants. They wore the orange and black like the two Molten they encountered in the Blacklore Woods. No weapons were visible on their person. The power they held at their fingertips was deadly enough.

Her back stung in a reminder of what their fire could do.

Unlike the two in the forest, though, these guards had various states of disintegrating skin, indicating the use of forbidden magic.

Part two of her job was up. Novak had needed a way to dispose of the guards quickly and quietly, and flooding the volcano or smashing them over the head with rocks would give them away too easily.

Crouching in the shadows, she took a deep breath, the cold night air filling her lungs. She wished she wasn't already feeling drained. It was hard to be around these four, who had so much practice with their powers and way more endurance than her.

Her body begged for rest, but her mind needed to move and burn all the anxiety away.

Taking in the monstrosity of a castle before them, Adelia felt as if her dad was farther from her than ever before. It seemed insurmountable. Doubts crept in that they couldn't get in, find him, and get out safely. She was just a girl from Bark Beach who went birdwatching on the weekends.

She wasn't a Fae warrior.

She didn't have what it took to save her dad.

He would spend the rest of his life, if he wasn't already dead, in this jail, wondering if his daughter had ever loved him enough to even try.

Her eyes stung as tears threatened to escape. Ash had been right when they first met. She didn't really know what was going on. She was winging it, running on pure adrenaline. And the reality of the situation hit her with the force of a punch to the gut. Panic flared in her chest, and she felt frozen. From her fingertips, up her arms, to her lungs, she was freezing over.

It was a cold panic.

She couldn't do this.

She wasn't strong enough.

As if sensing this, a steady hand landed on her shoulder. His warmth permeated from the gloves, warming her soul.

Ash was crouching beside her in the shadow of the castle. The lights from the castle reflected in his soft caramel eyes. He always seemed to sense her emotions at times like this.

He locked his eyes with hers and faith, trust, and confidence stared back at her. That and his reassuring touch seemed like a promise.

A promise that he trusted her, that he would be right here, that he wouldn't leave her in this hell alone.

It should have helped, but all she wanted to do was get out of here.

With him.

She wished she could go back to The Perch with him, where they were alone, and he acted like he wanted to be around her.

Right from the moment she met him, something about him had drawn her in. His eyes were filled with mystery that she could spend a lifetime solving.

He leaned down like he had on the cliff back at her house, his breath kissing the back of her neck, and whispered, "I know you're scared. But I know you can do this. You're brave and stronger than you know. I'm here to help you get your dad back, and I promise I won't leave. Just trust me." It was quiet enough that only she would be able to hear his words.

But he didn't know everything.

He didn't know she was bringing him into this deadly situation for her own selfish reasons.

He didn't know she already had the key.

He didn't know she had been keeping her own secrets.

She turned back to the castle looming above them and pictured her dad—beaten and broken in the dungeons. Starved and dying. The light missing from his eyes. She thought about how they would never bake cookies together again. How he would never call her Addy again. He would never pick her up in a bear hug and swing her around despite how much she protested and said she wasn't a child anymore.

There wasn't really an option.

Adelia guessed there never was.

She would do anything for him, including sneaking into a fortress of mad fire-breathing Molten Fae.

WITH ASH'S hand on her shoulder, she summoned the last of her energy and felt the air around the castle, warm from the sweltering heat of the lava. She felt the air surrounding the guards and each breath they took stories above her.

She didn't need to accomplish some crazy feat, just a small transfer of air. She focused on the air filling the lungs of the guard closest to her. She could feel the air as it made its way down his trachea, to his lungs, and into the smallest cells there, providing the body with the necessary oxygen to function.

And all she did was pull it out.

She pulled the oxygen back up his windpipe, leaving his lungs empty and screaming for air that wasn't there.

They saw his eyes widen, and he scratched at his throat, trying to scream but having no air to do it. Within seconds, he had fallen to his knees, unconscious, the other guards utterly oblivious to their fallen comrade.

In no time, every balcony stood vacant, as well as the main gate, after all the guards had silently fallen unconscious from asphyxiation.

Rory let out a low whistle. "Remind me to never get on your bad side, Adelia."

Ash moved his other hand to Adelia's shoulder and gave her a squeeze of encouragement. She smiled tiredly at him, exhaustion threatening to overtake her now more than ever.

They moved through the cover of night, followed by the ever silent Rin at Maewyn's side, and through the front doors. Adelia was silently praying she had taken out all the necessary obstacles because she didn't have the strength for any more right now. It seemed that Ash sensed this as he stayed close to her side despite the wide-open space of the castle foyer.

Maewyn scurried over to one of the unconscious guards and started to take off his jacket. Rory looked momentarily taken aback, his face going red at the indecency of the act. Maewyn, on the other hand, had no shame. She stripped him of his clothes and tossed them to Novak, who quickly threw the guard's uniforms over her sleek black clothes.

They made quick work of the other guards, each changing into the bolder but still less conspicuous orange and black outfits of the guards. While they changed, Rin made quick work of the guards by dragging them into the shadowed corners, hidden from view.

Maewyn looked like a child playing dress-up in her mother's clothes. The uniform fell off her shoulders, and she struggled to keep the pants up around her waist. The whole ensemble was three times too big for her slight frame, and she was drowning in fabric.

"Um... maybe it's better if I stay in my own clothes? If we run into anyone, you can say I'm a prisoner or something," she mumbled.

The group nodded solemnly, trying to stifle their chuckles.

"You look adorable, Maewyn," Rory tried to say seriously.

She furrowed her brows and put her hands on her hips. It was the farthest from intimidating that she could have possibly been. She looked like a little bright angelic version of Benjamin Button.

"Shut it. I don't need your sass right now," she whispered furiously. "I know I look like a child!"

"A violent, murderous child. If anyone came at you right now, you'd be able to knock them out with the force of your anger and embarrassment alone," Rory whispered back.

"I dare them to try," she seethed as she peeled off the uniform.

Rory threw his hands up in defense but turned away, still grinning.

From what they had discovered in their research, they knew

the general way to the dungeons and began to skulk through the castle's dim lantern-lit hallways. The inside of the castle was no less welcoming than the outside. The dark stone walls were lined with old flickering lanterns, lighting every few metres in a pool of pale yellow light. The castle must have been grand at one time. However, now it was showing the marks of time and disrepair. Sections of the uniform stone crumbled onto the floor, cobwebs were visible where the lamplight shone, and charcoal velvet curtains cascaded down to block the moonlight.

She was walking the halls of the blood-stained Molten Fae.

Terrible creatures who were mad with magic walked these halls—called this home.

She could hear their whispers of anger from being locked away from the world.

She could hear the mounting cries of victory at the gate's recent fall.

They were hungry for revenge and thirsty for retribution.

She could only hope to avoid them as they descended into the belly of the beast.

THEY TURNED the corner into the section of the castle where Novak knew the stairs to the dungeon would be.

"Come on, hurry up. No one is out right now, but we can't dally," she whispered. She pulled the hood of the uniform up over her blue hair to better stay hidden. All they could see under the shadows were her swirling ocean-like eyes that darted across the castle, looking for threats. She picked up her pace and rounded the corner, coming face to face with a Fae.

She had appeared out of nowhere, and they hadn't heard her approaching.

Oh, this is bad.

It was a middle-aged Fae woman, her hair greying at the

roots, faint wrinkles at the corners of her eyes. She was wearing a stark white lab coat that was blinding in the dark, barely lit hallway. Faint black streaks were visible around her collar as if her veins were necrotic and the sickness was spreading. She looked as if death was reaching its arms out for her, but she wasn't ready to give up her ghost yet.

Rory made to grab Maewyn's arms behind her to give the illusion of her being a captive, hoping the other woman hadn't seen. The rest of them were in guard uniforms and hoped it

would work as cover. At the same time, Rin darted for the shadows, small enough to hide without being seen despite his bright white fur.

The woman looked at the five of them carefully, but then her gaze landed on Maewyn. Maewyn had her eyes downcast and shoulders drooped, playing the perfect part of a beaten, broken prisoner. The woman's eyes brightened with a mixture of surprise and delight at the sight of her.

"Did the sentries Queen Karai send out already return with a Fae for me?" Her excitement was audible in her voice.

Confusion washed through Adelia while she stood there frozen.

The sentries? Like the ones we encountered in the forest?

She wondered what this woman could want with Maewyn when the castle was normally teeming with Molten. But now that she thought back to the Fae in the forest, they had mentioned bringing something back. The thought of them kidnapping anyone to bring to this dark, desolate place was chilling. They already had her dad. Why did they need more?

The Molten woman then reached out to grab Maewyn from Rory's hands. He reluctantly loosened his grip, a protest on the tip of his tongue, but she continued speaking, unaware of his reluctance. "I thought she had only sent them out a few days ago, but no matter. This is brilliant. I'll be taking her down to the lab now. Many thanks!"

Giddy with excitement, she steered Maewyn away from the team, roughly holding her hands trapped behind her back. The woman glanced back at them with a malicious grin on her face. She still believed they were all guards. She winked at them before she made her way back down the hallway with Maewyn in tow.

Maewyn stole one last glance at her team. True panic was written across her features, and a silent scream hung on her open lips.

CHAPTER 27

"What just happened?" Adelia hissed. "Why in the world did she *request* a non-Molten Fae for her lab? Who even was that?"

Novak, ever calm and calculating, was the first to compose herself after Maewyn was led away. "Okay, I know we originally planned to stay together, but we don't have that option now. Rory and I are going after Maewyn. Ash and Adelia, you two head to the dungeons. With any luck, Teilio is there, and you can get in and out quickly. We don't have long before those guards wake up, so get going."

"We're splitting up again?" Adelia asked quietly, and Novak nodded.

"We really can't afford not to. The longer we spend in the heart of the enemy, the more we risk being found. We're like a virus. It won't be long until the host realizes we aren't one of them."

Adelia wondered if Novak was indeed as calm as she appeared. She portrayed no hint of worry—the perfect leader as always. Had she ever known failure?

Everything from the way she held herself, to the way she spoke with unfailing confidence, conveyed that failure was not an option. She instilled the group with sureness in a way Adelia never could. She had never been a born leader, preferring to work alone. She had avoided people more after her peers became cruel to her, ridiculing her for not liking typical teenager things ike parties and name-brand fashion.

But despite the pang of jealousy at Novak's leadership, she also respected it. She wasn't sure when her feelings of apprehension and distrust about them all had changed, but she knew she cared for Maewyn.

She agreed they needed to split up. There was no way they were leaving her behind. She and Ash would have to be careful on their own, especially due to her drained power levels.

Without waiting for a reply from the team about her plan to split up, Novak made to follow the mysterious woman. Rory and the distressed Rin followed behind her, leaving Ash and Adelia alone in the dim light.

She would have to trust Novak's decision and their abilities to handle this separately.

Ash let out a breath he must have been holding, almost in relief. Though Adelia couldn't imagine what he was relieved about. He glanced at her and nodded as if to say follow me. She crept along behind him, watching him move with practiced stealth through the shadows again.

She could see his toned muscles shifting under the guard uniform as he moved.

Is it weird to be thinking about how good he looks in the orange and black uniform right now?

Probably.

She should be focused on being stealthy, but the colours complemented his grey hair so perfectly.

They reached the dungeons with no other interruptions and

descended the dank spiralling staircase into what felt like the pits of Hell. The temperature grew hotter with each step they took, and the thick air stuck to her skin.

Once they were at the base of the stairs, all they could see were the few feet in front of them thanks to the light from the stairwell. Droppings littered the floor, and she swore something crawled over her foot in the dark. The smell of death was so thick, she could taste it—it was pungent.

Ash grabbed a torch off the wall by the stairs, lifting it to bathe the room in the flickering light. Cautiously, they advanced into the darkness. It would be horrible for her father down here. It was like being trapped inside a crematory. The stifling heat would dehydrate a person long before they starved down here.

Ash approached the first cell and lifted the light to illuminate the interior. Adelia held her breath, hoping they'd see a person inside—more specifically her father. It was so quiet, though, it was hard to imagine anyone was down here.

The cell was empty.

Releasing the breath, they moved on to the second cell. Then the third.

All the cramped stone cells they checked were empty.

The only things occupying them were the rats and their shadows.

Her hope waned with each empty cell until there was only one left.

Ash paused before passing his light before it, undoubtedly feeling the same apprehension. They all assumed her dad would be down here. She was beginning to realize how naïve it was to assume their plans would have no hiccups. The only problem was that if he wasn't down here, then he was likely already dead, and that wasn't a thought she wanted to entertain.

As Ash brought the light before the final cell, a pair of blue eyes shone back at them from the dark.

Out from the darkness, a man stepped into the light.

But it wasn't her father.

It was a young man, close in age to Ash and Adelia. Despite the desolate conditions of the dungeons, his eyes were still bright and assessing. He stared with an uncomfortable intensity at Ash, unblinking. Adelia could see the gears shifting behind his eyes, calculating. Without taking his eyes off Ash, he grinned slyly as if he was in on some big secret that no one else was.

Ash broke eye contact with him and grabbed Adelia's arm to pull her away from the man and back out of the dungeons, but then he spoke.

His voice was hoarse and raspy as if he hadn't spoken in years. "Don't you want to know where he is?"

Adelia halted in her tracks and ripped her arm out of Ash's grasp to turn back to the piercing blue eyes of the stranger before her. He had moved to the front of the cell, the dim light of their torch lighting him fully now. He was lean but healthy-looking, indicating he hadn't been down here long, but his skin was covered in grey ash, giving it a sickly look. He had high cheekbones and a sharp jawline still visible beneath his dark stubble. It was impossible to tell what colour his hair was beneath all the dirt and grime.

"What did you say?" she asked him hesitantly.

He smirked again. "You look just like him. The man they had down here with me. Same sunshiny hair and 'no one can stop me once I put my mind to something' attitude. Frankly, people like that exhaust me a bit. Anyway, they took him not too long ago."

It was like her heart stopped. The world stood still while she processed the information.

Her dad was alive.

He was here.

She wasn't too late.

She couldn't even try to hide the relief that flooded her features.

He continued, "Don't get it into your pretty little head that I'm going to tell you this for free, though." His smirk morphed into more of a feral grin, his eyes lighting up in anticipation of what he was going to say next. "All you have to do is get me out of here and take me with you. We'll stop by where they took him on the way out, and we can all leave here. Happily. Ever. After."

Ash tugged on Adelia's arm, trying to pull her away. He looked scared like he knew she was actually considering this. "No way, Adelia, we can't," he hissed. "We can't trust him. Look at him! He's half-feral, a literal prisoner in the Molten dungeon. We don't need him."

Adelia kept her eyes on the prisoner before her. "That's what you said about me when you first met me. *We don't need her.* Well, it turns out you needed me." There was fire in her eyes when she looked at him, but he said nothing. "We don't have to do this alone. We already lost Maewyn and had to split up from the group. We could save time if this guy knows where my dad is!"

She flung her hands out in exasperation. The first part of the plan was executed seamlessly, but having Maewyn taken was a disaster. Small, delicate Maewyn with her disconcerting icy eyes and child-like demeanour. She was the team's life and energy, and Adelia knew if they didn't get her back, they would never be the same. She knew she would never forgive herself. She was the one who led them here on a wild goose chase for a 'missing key.'

Yes, it was probably risky to let this boy out, but he was a prisoner, wasn't he? It's not like it was a trap. The Molten didn't know they were coming, so he wasn't put here to trick them or capture them for the Queen. It was a risk she was willing to take. And for some reason, the wild look in his eyes didn't convey malice. He seemed more thrilled with the prospect of just being free.

She waited for Ash to argue. She waited for him to tell her it was a foolish plan, or that he couldn't believe she was even considering it. Instead, he seemed resigned like he couldn't quite believe it himself that he was going to trust her in this despite his own reservations.

He gave the prisoner a hard look, as hard as the basalt stone of the volcano around them. His eyes glinted red, a fire igniting inside. "If you even think about betraying us to the Molten, I will kill you without hesitation. You will die in this forsaken place, and they will roast your body over the river and eat your organs for breakfast."

Adelia believed him.

She wasn't sure if he just made all that up or if that's actually what the Molten did to their dead, but his threat promised suffering, death, and no mercy. It was intended to scare the prisoner into being submissive, and she thought he succeeded.

Ash was imposing and authoritative in how he spoke, like he could command an entire room of subjects to kneel before him. As impressed as she was, though, Adelia wasn't sure if the prisoner was afraid. He seemed more amused by the threat than alarmed.

The prisoner replied, "Of course." He bowed low at the hips, still grinning in amusement.

Ash gave Adelia a pointed look of exasperation, clear he still didn't agree, but for her sake, he would.

"One quick word, though, before we do this," Ash said and motioned at Adelia to come with him out of earshot of the prisoner. They huddled along the wall around the corner again, next to the stairs.

"Whatever you do, don't turn your back to this guy. I don't trust him, Adelia. He might bring us to your dad, but be ready for a catch. I'll lead the group, him in the middle, and you'll bring up the rear. If anything goes wrong, promise me you'll run. Your strength is with ranged attacks, not melee. So get somewhere safer, and then you can use your powers to help from there."

He reached out and tucked a strand of her hair behind an ear. The light brush of his fingers against her skin sent a small jolt of electricity through her veins.

"You have to trust me," he whispered, his eyes dropping to her lips for an imperceptible moment.

"I do," she whispered back, the truth of the statement filling her heart. "Looks like you might even trust me a little bit too." She flashed him a smirk that rivaled his own.

"Or maybe I just can't say no to those doe eyes of yours." He took her hands and pressed one of his daggers into them. "Just in case."

Then he pulled her back around the corner towards the prisoner and pulled out his sword, which shone with a bright white angelic glow in the dark.

She would have to ask him about it one day. She was curious why it shone like that, how even at his side, it could light a dark room.

He put it into the cell's lock and shifted it around until a soft click was heard and the padlock fell away. The iron bars of the cell swung upon, and the prisoner sauntered out.

He clapped Ash on the back with a dull thud. "Let's go get him then, shall we?"

. . .

A HEAVY SILENCE settled over the three of them. Adelia had so many questions for the young prisoner, like why he was locked up, how he knew where her dad was, or even what his name was, but the threat of being discovered outweighed her mounting curiosity.

The stranger led them through a maze of hallways deeper into the heart of the volcano and farther away from the rest of the team. Adelia quickly lost her sense of direction as the identical cold stone walls blurred past. The castle was barren. No décor hung on the walls. It was just the cold, empty stone. It was like a snakeskin—empty, old, and a shadow of what it used to be.

Ash also seemed to be holding back his tongue. He kept glancing back at Adelia as if he wanted to tell her something but then thought better of it and kept moving. His muscles were taut, and his movements were stiff as if his body was fighting his every step.

Contrastingly, the prisoner walked with ease. Adelia wanted to tell him to crouch, to move slower, and stay in the shadows, but he seemed to be riding high on freedom and was not concerned with the consequences of being caught.

Either that, or he was leading them straight to Molten guards. Adelia surveyed him as best as she could in the dark and decided he didn't *look* Molten? She hadn't encountered too many, but most had traces of forbidden magic marring their skin, like ink was running through their arteries instead of blood. Either that or they had fully transformed into the monstrous creatures they had fought back at her house.

The prisoner's shirt was tattered and ripped, but beneath was smooth, tanned, unblemished skin, and in the light of the torches, his hair was a dark chocolate colour. He looked healthy minus the surface cuts and the coating of dirt and grime on his skin like paraffin wax.

As they began to descend a widening hallway, they found themselves before a large black metal door with the same pattern as the small key hanging from Adelia's neck. It had a colossal presence, dwarfing them in size.

She felt like it was staring down at them, judging them.

Looking up, Adelia could see it sat flush with the frame, with no handles or knob to indicate how to open it.

The prisoner's feral grin grew in intensity, and he stepped forward and pushed the double doors wide, groaning with the effort. The doors swung open to reveal a grand throne room.

A throne room that was most definitely *not* empty.

The Queen of the Molten sat upon her throne, looking down at none other than Teilio Larson sprawled on the floor before her. The entire room was full of guards, courtiers, and royalty alike, who all looked up in unison as the doors banged open. Adelia and Ash stood there, bewildered, fully exposed, with a dawning realization that they hadn't encountered anyone else in the castle because they were all here. Every single Molten Fae that resided in this castle was in this room, and they had let themselves be willingly brought here. And there was no running away now.

CHAPTER 28

MAEWYN

Maewyn felt as if she were reliving her childhood as she was led handcuffed down the dim, empty halls of the Molten castle. Before the war, she had grown up in the small, reclusive Snow Court and thus was far removed from the majority of the fighting during the Molten War. She grew up in the castle. Her father was a cousin of the Snow King, but they were as close as brothers. She spent her childhood attending balls and feasts, where she would laugh, giggle, and drink ginger ale that looked like champagne, to feel like an adult.

It was easy to live a life of privilege as she did and never give much thought to the world outside the Ice Castle until she was older and the war began.

She remembered her father and the Snow King secluded in a cold drawing room, planning a defence strategy for the Snow Court. The fighting was restricted to the Molten and the Wind Courts for the time being, but they all knew Queen Karai would soon begin attacking the other courts. If only because they were staying neutral.

She would try and bring hot cocoa to her father and uncle, hoping it would help relax them and maybe her father would take a break and come play with her. But she was always shooed away. The servants led her away from the room, saying he was busy, she would have to entertain herself, or that it was healthy to spend time alone sometimes.

But she never felt like that. When she was alone, memories of her mother surfaced. She would remember how her mom smiled, a crooked, toothy grin, laugh wrinkles around her mouth and corners of her eyes. Her mother never really fit in at the court, never caring to wear traditional snow gowns like the other ladies, but rather tunics and warm sweaters to beat the cold. She spent all her time with Maewyn. She was determined to teach Maewyn how to fend for herself, how to hold a sword and throw a punch, while all the other children of the court learned to hold teacups and curtsy like proper young ladies.

She had always felt the heavy glares and judgement when they walked down the frosty halls of the castle, but it never mattered because her mom was there. Her mother walked through those halls as if she were the Snow Queen herself, and Maewyn looked at her as if she were. She always thought her mom would make a great queen. She was kind and accepting, and she believed that women were as capable as the men of the court.

Her mom had always said, *If we stand up for ourselves, we are really standing up for all women. Maybe today they are walking the halls as ghosts, afraid to be more than they are told, but perhaps they will have the courage tomorrow. The courage to step outside society's cage and be themselves. Don't judge the girls here. We need to stick together, my snowflake. You need to focus on being yourself, and maybe one day it will help other women realize they can too.*

After her mom got sick, it was hard to keep thinking that. It was as if the Snow Court had punished her for going against the grain, for continually defying the unwritten rules for the women of the court. Maewyn fell into those rules for a while after her mother's death. She had felt like a ghost of her former self, unsure how to live her life without her mom there with her. Her heart felt fractured, like a frozen pond cracking beneath the weight of freshly fallen snow.

That was when she had tried to reach out to her father, and it was good for a while. He was comforting and held her tight on the hard days, as if he was trying to hold her broken parts together, to keep her from falling apart. But that was when there was peace, and his duties in the court were few.

When the war began, he chose work. He chose work over her, and she slowly found herself alone more and more. She used to walk outside in the courtyard, hoping to clear her head, but would see something that reminded her of her mother, and she would have to stop. She would sit down in the cold snow, pressing her back against the cold garden gate. She would sit there until her fingers were numb, and she was shivering violently. She could feel her sense of self fragmenting, her very essence breaking like an ice cube dropped on a cold tile floor. She didn't know how to pick up the pieces alone. She had felt abandoned and was tempted to just lay her head down on the frozen pathway and close her eyes.

That was when she had decided. There was nothing left for her in the Snow Court. It had stopped being her home the day her mom had died.

She had applied to the Faerie Guard the next day. The skills her mother had taught her proved useful, and soon she found herself learning how to be herself again. She had been placed with Novak, Rory, and Ash, and they became her new family. They brought her onto their team, and she had felt wanted again, useful. Like they needed her. Then she had found Rin and the energetic arctic fox had filled her heart the rest of the way.

The dark days were few and far between now, and without ever speaking about it, Rory seemed to know precisely when they were. He would wordlessly take her into one of his big hugs, and she would bury her head into his chest. She had grown accustomed to the Snow Fae's icy skin, never having felt a warm hug before Rory. She hadn't realized how comforting a hug could be. She had told herself the team would be together forever.

But now, she found herself alone again. The others hadn't had a choice, but it didn't make it any easier. The woman had handcuffed her to a bed deep within the Molten Court. Except it wasn't a bed for sleeping, it was like an operating table, and she was surrounded by bubbling, smoking flasks and equipment reminiscent of a laboratory. The woman had strapped her arms and legs down, completely immobilizing her and preventing her from using her powers.

The woman hadn't spoken much other than mumble to herself quietly. The only things Maewyn could make out were *yes, yes, it should work,* or *mhmm yes, the arm.*

The woman's eyes were wild, and she looked delirious with fever. Sweat dripped from her forehead as she scuffled around the room, collecting various items and putting them onto a cold metal rolling cart. The closer Maewyn watched her, the more she appeared to be in pain. Each step was jerky, and her hands trembled with the effort. Once she had gathered all the necessary equipment, she rolled the cart over to the bedside, the rusty wheels squealing with each turn.

On the tray lay a large syringe filled with a deep red liquid. At first glance, it looked like blood, but then Maewyn saw the texture. It was bubbling and thick like the lava of the Molten river. Coursing through it were veins of black, matching the ones on the woman's skin. It looked like a swirling tornado of black and crimson.

She needed out. *Now.*

The others weren't going to get here quickly enough. She knew they wouldn't leave her here, but they wouldn't act rashly either. If only she could get her hands loose enough to flick her wrist. She could freeze the cuffs, making them easy to break. However, as she thrashed and jerked, they would not yield.

The woman had moved beside Maewyn, lifting the syringe to inject whatever the mysterious liquid was into her.

A quiet sob escaped from Maewyn. "Why?! Why are you doing this?"

The woman looked up from the syringe, and what seemed like guilt skirted across her features for a brief second. "I'm sorry, dear, I have to." Her hands trembled as if she could will them to stop. Her eyes filled with a sudden sadness.

Wordlessly, she flicked her glance upward, and Maewyn followed her gaze. Up in the corner of the room was a small camera. Whirring and spinning, it surveyed the laboratory and its occupants. The woman bent down close to Maewyn's ear. "If I don't do this, she'll kill me. Or they'll lock me up and stop me from using magic as a punishment. And I *need* to use it." Her whispering became more hysterical with every word.

Maewyn knew from first glance that this woman had practiced forbidden magic, but she had no idea that Queen Karai was using it as a means of torture. If this woman didn't follow the Queen's orders, she would be locked up, unable to get her fix, and at this late in the game, it would probably kill her.

Maewyn looked again at the spiderweb of black veins on her skin, her sickly grey complexion and knew it would not be long before this woman became consumed by forbidden magic madness. She would do anything to continue to practice forbidden magic. It was probably how she made the liquid in the syringe. It was like nothing Maewyn had ever seen before.

Then she abruptly grabbed Maewyn's arm and began to inject the fluid.

It came as such a shock, mainly because Maewyn had convinced herself that her friends would burst through the door before anything bad happened.

Within seconds, all her thoughts were consumed as the fluid began to flow through her.

It was a fire in her veins, and she screamed so shrilly she was surprised the glass syringe didn't break. It felt as if her blood had become acid, burning and searing with each excruciating pulse of her heart. She writhed and attempted to pull away from the iron grip of the woman. The syringe was half empty now, and the women continued to methodically pump more fluid into Maewyn. Her vision clouded over, and the world around her became dim as blackness threatened to overtake her. She had never experienced pain like this before. The fracturing of her soul after her mother had died was close, but this was acute. It was fire where that was ice. She thought her skin was turning to ash, like she was burning alive—and then it happened.

She heard a bang as the doors of the laboratory flew open, and Rory and Novak rushed in. She could barely form a thought other than that they were too late.

They had waited too long, and she would turn to dust and ash in this hospital bed.

They had left her alone, and now she was dying.

The world darkened at the periphery and then went black.

CHAPTER 29

Adelia could smell the odour of metallic blood when the door opened. It was so thick in the air, she could taste it on her tongue. Her father was lying in a puddle, his face a mask of red when he lifted his head slowly to lock eyes with hers.

Her heart shattered at the sight. She had never seen him look so defeated, so helpless, before in her life. She hadn't been prepared for this. She hadn't been prepared to see him look like he had given up already. The light had already left his bright eyes. What had they done to him in the short time he had been here? How did they break him so easily?

The Queen was sitting upon her basalt throne. The lofty chair towered above them, set with obsidian jewels that glittered like the night sky. The Queen herself was terrifyingly elegant to match. It was clear she used to be the textbook definition of beautiful, with high cheekbones and a long, lean, elegant frame. Her nose was sharp and accentuated like a hawk's beak and her long hair flowed down her back in waves of grey that matched the smoke drifting from the sconces along the wall.

Her use of forbidden magic had stripped that beauty away, and what was left was clearly a shell of who she once was. Similar to the monsters that had attacked her house, the Queen's skin was charred and black, split open across the face in what looked like a large gash. Flakes of charred skin scattered the throne and ground around her, like smoking dandruff that covered the ground. She was wearing a long, glittering black gown that cascaded onto the floor, with an intricate black bodice that barely covered her shoulders to expose more volcanic skin. Atop her head sat a black crown that looked as if it had been placed upon her upside down. The large spokes of a typical crown protruded downward to make it look like she was crying large black jeweled teardrops.

She had been laughing before the doors had banged open, but now confusion darted across her steely features.

The courtiers around her had fallen silent, the tension in the room almost as thick as the stench of blood.

As the Queen regained composure, she rose with a fluid grace from the throne and stalked toward the pair. Adelia looked around in a panic, only to find the large doors they had come through had already closed shut. There was nowhere to go.

She had no delusions that she and Ash could escape from a room filled with a hundred Molten Fae.

The Queen's grin, dripping with acid, grew as she sauntered past Teilio, who was trying to push himself up off the floor and onto his elbows with visible effort. She levelled a kick at him that sent him sprawling to the floor again, coughing up more blood.

Adelia couldn't help the cry of terror that escaped her lips as she lunged forward, but Ash held her back.

Couldn't she see he was already hurt? Why did she need to inflict more pain?

The Queen halted in front of them, appraising Ash with reverent glances. She seemed breathless and excited. She held her hands out to Ash, palms up, as if she expected him to pass her something. Adelia felt Ash release her, and he locked his steely eyes with hers. There were a thousand unspoken words written across his face, regret, longing, and a desire for her to understand.

She knew then that he must be telling her they were going to die.

There was so much left unsaid between them, and she wanted to tell him she was sorry. She was sorry for bringing him here. Sorry for not telling him the truth about the key. Sorry for pushing him on his past when he wasn't ready to talk about it. Sorry they wouldn't have more time.

The look in his eyes seemed to echo those thoughts as he reached out and placed his hands in the Queen's.

Gingerly, the Molten Queen removed his gloves, slowly peeling them away from each finger.

Confusion flooded Adelia's thoughts.

Ash never removed his gloves, just like he never went anywhere without his sword. They were a part of him.

The tight gloves fell to the floor, revealing his hands.

The hands Adelia thought about time and time again. The hands that had always held hers so surely when she needed him.

The hands that were cracked and peeling with charred, molten skin like the Queen before him.

CHAPTER 30

The Queen lifted her lifeless eyes to meet Ash's. She was gripping his hands in hers, a faint tremor visible.

"It is you," she whispered, her scratchy voice barely audible. There was true emotion behind her eyes now, and Adelia's own head began to roar.

The Queen continued, "I thought you were dead. I thought you were dead!" And she pulled Ash into an embrace, so much like the one Adelia was dying to have with her father. The emotional embrace dragged on and finally the Queen placed her hands on Ash's shoulders and pushed him back. Her eyes roved over his face, his outfit and weapons, as if assessing him for the first time.

Orange liquid began to leak from her eyes, and she wiped it with her sleeve, causing it to smear all over her black dress.

She composed herself with a visibly shaky breath and said, "Today is a joyous day." She turned to the silenced courtiers around her. "The barrier is broken, we will soon be free and"— she paused for dramatic effect—"my son has returned home!"

. . .

THE SHOCKED EXPRESSIONS of the Molten were evident as they all looked at Ash with renewed fervor. Their greedy eyes drank him in and the looks of realization spread across the crowd. Soon, cheering and clapping erupted from the courtiers, only adding to the roaring in Adelia's ears.

Adelia looked at Ash standing beside her. He was immobilized with fear, as if Maewyn had frozen the blood in his veins. She waited for him to deny it, to say the Queen had the wrong person, but the heavy silence stretched on, and he refused to meet her gaze.

Look at me, Ash, she willed. *Tell me it's not true.*

But he didn't look at her.

He smiled at the Queen then, and the mask he wore snapped back on. The fear was gone. It was as if she had imagined it, like it was just a trick of the light on his features. Maybe it had never been a mask at all. Maybe the kindness, the small smiles she glimpsed were the real mask.

He made a sweeping bow to the crowd before him as they clapped and applauded. One visibly emotional girl in the front put a hand over her mouth and was slumped over in shock across another woman's arms.

This couldn't be true. Ash was Molten? Not only was he Molten, he was *a prince?* Adelia tried desperately to convince herself that it couldn't be true, but even as she tried, the pieces of the puzzle began to fall into place.

How he refused to ever use his powers.

How he refused to talk about his past.

The gloves to hide his scars.

How the ground heated up mysteriously when he was having nightmares.

How he had seemed more nervous than the rest of them to come to the Molten Court on this mission.

"Ash..." she whispered, looking up at him. He finally returned her gaze, and she saw it in his eyes then.

It was true.

He stepped forward then, in front of Adelia to block her slightly from the room that was dripping with anticipation, waiting for him to speak. He moved with the same air he had down in the dungeons, with the aura of a true prince.

"Citizens of Molten. I have returned home. The gates were open and I seized my chance to cross the river and return. It has been many tumultuous years since I was last here. Many believed I died in the war. However, I can assure you, I am here and I will do everything in my power to assist my mother in our goal of reclaiming our spot in Faerie." His voice echoed around the room.

The crowd roared, the hooting and hollering of the monstrous Fae around her a cacophony of noise.

The Queen beckoned him to her once more. "All these years, I grieved, thinking my only son perished in the war. But here you are. Grown up and handsome as ever. I'd recognize those eyes anywhere. And just look at this skin as smooth as the stone beneath me." She brushed her crusted hand across her face, as if in longing.

She lowered her voice to a whisper that Adelia could barely hear, "As soon as I saw those gloves, though, I knew you'd done forbidden magic. You truly are my son." She raised her voice again. "And not only has he returned"—she gestured to Adelia —"but he has brought us a gift!"

Ash glanced over his shoulder at Adelia, his face cold and calculating.

She couldn't bear to meet his traitorous eyes.

She looked away to survey the room, the barren walls and empty floor. Other than her father, broken and bleeding on the floor, and the Molten along the walls, the room was vacant.

There was no indication that this had been a feast, or a ball. It was evident the crowd had gathered for the sole purpose of watching their enemy be tortured and executed.

A flicker of movement caught Adelia's eye from where her father lay, and a small iridescent red and orange snake weaseled its way from under her father's arm and slithered over to Ash's leg.

"Atheris..." he whispered. It slithered up his leg and coiled around his neck, its large globular turquoise eyes appraising him. The viper's tongue forked out, tickling his ear, and Ash drew back up to his full height.

Standing before a crowd of people, with a viper around his shoulders and his charred hands visible at his sides, Adelia found that she was afraid of him for the first time.

The Prince of the Molten Fae.

His powers must be unrivalled. He could probably scorch a person alive from the inside out with just a thought. When she had met him, he had been far from welcoming, but he had begrudgingly accepted her into their small group. Before this, she had even thought he might like her. But clearly, that had all been a ploy. This whole time he had been angling to return home and reclaim his throne. She had never mattered to him and the realization was heartbreaking.

It was unnerving how much she had truly started to care for him. His mischievous smirk that made her smile despite herself, and his strong presence that had made her feel safe. He had weaseled his way into her heart and she had trusted him.

She had never expected that the Molten Prince had been masquerading in the Faerie Guard since the war, biding his time to return home.

The Queen's voice brought her back to the present. "...With the daughter of our greatest enemy at that." Her depthless black gaze landed on Adelia, and she blinked slowly, her eyelids sliding against her eyeballs like sandpaper. "Don't think I didn't notice. You are his spitting image. You are just the motivation he needed." Her voice dripped with venom. This woman was so unlike the Ash she knew that it was hard to accept this could be his mother. But then again, the Ash she knew didn't exist. There was no Faerie Guard named Ash. He had always been Ash, the Molten Prince.

The court had been locked away for decades with no contact to the rest of Faerie. Adelia doubted anyone realized the Prince hadn't been locked away with the others. Adelia recalled the memory of her father's, about how the key had only partially worked. The Molten within the court, including the Queen, had been locked away inside their own home, but all the others remained free. Massacre had ensued and without reinforcements from the Molten Court, the first wave of soldiers were defeated by the Wind Court. She wondered why he wasn't at the Molten Court when the war broke out.

She was ripped from her thoughts when the Queen screamed, "Grab her!"

Molten guards rushed forward from either side, pinning Adelia's arms behind her roughly. The heat of their fiery skin was palpable through the guard uniform she still wore. The guard who grabbed her hands kicked at her knees roughly and she crumpled to the ground helplessly as both her leg and prosthetic gave out.

Pain lanced through her one kneecap at the impact on the unforgiving hot stone floor. The guard lifted a large black boot and pressed it into the semi-healed burns across her back to hold her down. The slowly healing scabs ripped open, sending searing pain across her back.

Warm blood leaked from the wound as he pushed his boot further into her spine with unforgiving force. She felt as if her spine would break under the weight.

The guard bent down and she could feel the heat wafting off of him.

"Such a pretty thing. Maybe the Queen will let us play with you after she's done with you," he snarled into her ear.

"Over my dead body, you monster." She threw her head back and her skull connected with his nose.

"You little bitch!" He grabbed her by the hair to yank her head back and expose her head. "You'll pay for that," he growled and spat a glob of fiery salvia onto her.

It burned on impact and the world began to spin. The force of his weight on her back, the impact from hitting him, and his burning saliva were too much.

Adelia was going to murder the prisoner who brought them here. How could she have been so foolish? She thought back to a few moments before, and there really was no reason she should have trusted him. He just played the right cards. He made her think he could bring her to her father and that had clouded her judgement. She didn't even know where he had gone.

She tried to move her head to look around the room, but as soon as she moved her neck, it sent lancing pain down her back all the way to her toes, and her vision blurred.

The hopelessness of the situation began to dawn on her as she lay on the floor with her skin pressed to the stone. She had come here thinking she was invincible. That she could infiltrate a highly dangerous court of powerful Fae to save her dad. She had never really doubted that they would succeed, but it had been a fool's mission all along.

She was no less a fool than before. Having powers and discovering she was a Fae didn't change any of that. She never took the time to think about consequences, and now she had condemned everyone to death.

Well, everyone but Ash, she thought bitterly.

She could only pray Ash wasn't being serious when he said

the Molten would cook people over the river and eat their organs. But now that she knew he was actually Molten, she worried there had been some truth behind the threat.

As she lay there on the ground, the imprint of the Molten key pressed into her chest. She didn't even want to think about what the Queen would do when she found it. It would most likely be destroyed, all hope of stopping the Molten from attacking the Wind Court again lost with it.

It meant her dad gave up his powers for nothing.

It meant he had given up his life in the Wind Court for nothing, and after seeing it firsthand, she knew that couldn't have been an easy decision.

As the world continued to darken, her thoughts drifted in an attempt to distract herself from the pain. Her vision was blurred around the edges and visions of her father flashed before her eyes. She began to wonder what her father had been like when he was a full Fae. Could he have made the wind bend to his every will? Could he fly weightless on wind currents of his own creation? He would have been able to throw this asshole guard off her back in a second.

It made more sense to her now why he had chosen their house in Bark Beach. Their small cottage on the cliff, where you could feel the ocean breeze kissing your skin. It was likely a way for him to experience what he had lost and feel somewhat connected to his home again. She ached to be back there, baking in the kitchen with him, completely unaware of the Molten Fae or a mysterious little key that was keeping them imprisoned.

She had lived her whole life until now, unaware there was another world beyond the one she knew. Her dad had kept that part of him from her, *for* her. At first, when she found out about his past, she had been hurt and confused. It had felt like a betrayal, that her father hadn't trusted her enough to share this part of himself. But she was wiser now and realized how he was protecting her. He kept her safe from the danger that crept in the shadows here and the deadly secrets everyone harboured.

The guard above her pressed down on her spine again in amusement. She faintly heard a hoarse, strangled cry erupt from her dad. In response, he was met with a foot to the face, which silenced him again abruptly as fresh blood poured from his already broken nose. He coughed and sputtered, unable to lift his hands to staunch the bleeding.

They would die here.

Before now, she'd had hope in her heart like the promising whisper of warm spring winds on a cold winter day. Like a promise that things would get better, but that hope had been dashed.

There would be no end to this dark, desolate place.

They would die here.

They were just two people, surrounded by guards, Molten Fae, and the most powerful Fae Queen in all of Faerie—her charred, cracking skin proof of how far she would go to hold onto that title.

Then Adelia felt the pressure from her back lift and thought for a moment the guard was letting up. Then she was met with a foot to the skull that rattled her jaw and everything went dark.

CHAPTER 31

Adelia woke to a throbbing headache. The kind you wake up with after an intense day of birding, when you spend eight hours with your neck craned up, searching the top of trees. They called it warbler neck. She tried to reach her hand up to her temple and hold some pressure there to ease the pain, only to find her hands had been handcuffed behind her back.

The events of the past day returned and she realized she must have eventually succumbed to unconsciousness back in the throne room.

All she remembered was being knocked to the floor by a Molten Guard and not much after that.

She awkwardly squirmed into a sitting position to take inventory of where she was and quickly realized she was back in the Molten dungeon but on the opposite side of the bars this time. She had been thrown into one of the cells, the light from the torch near the stairs barely warming her toes.

How could she have been this foolish? To think she could

break into a castle and save her dad. How did she ever think she could trust Ash?

She was a certified idiot.

"Adelia?" a voice whispered from her left and with a sob, she saw her father sitting on the ground in the cell across the hall.

His face was still bloodied, but it was drying. He had blood crusting across his forehead, and his nose appeared broken. His top lip was puffy and swollen. Dark purple bruises littered his neck and collarbone, but despite all this, he looked relieved. Relieved to see she was alive, which made her wonder how long she had been unconscious for.

Adelia didn't share his relief, though; he was broken and bloody, trapped behind the bars in a dungeon.

"Oh, God. *Dad.*" Tears prickling the back of her eyes again. She wanted to hug him, to reassure herself that he was here and he was real. The dam holding back her tears broke and she couldn't stop the river.

Her tears turned to sobs that echoed through the dungeon.

Adelia wept until she was gasping for air, each shuddering intake of breath echoing across the cold, empty dungeon walls. Her tears mixed with the dirt and grime that covered her face, and it only intensified the headache.

She cried hysterically because there was no one there to witness it but her dad.

He hushed her as soothingly as he could from his own cell, but he couldn't reach out and hold her. She would never hug her dad again. They would die down here in the dark. She could feel herself spiraling into a black hole of hopelessness. Eventually, her tears dried, leaving behind a hollow emptiness.

"Oh, Dad, I'm so sorry," she whispered, her voice hoarse from sobbing.

"Addy. Addy, my sunshine. You have *nothing* to be sorry for." He moved as close to the bars as he could and she wanted nothing more than to reach out and touch him. To hug him and hold him. He felt so far away despite his closeness.

"Addy, I should have told you. I should have told you everything. I'm so sorry. I never meant to drag you into this. I... I just wanted you to have a good life. A happy life, away from the horrors I witnessed here. What is *still* going on here."

She shook her head. "I thought I could save you, Dad. I thought I could trust *him*." She choked on the word him, unable to even say his name out loud. "But I was naive. And now we are going to die."

He smiled a sorrowful smile. "Honey, you did save me. Every day of your life you saved me. You saved me from my past that haunted me, with your bright smile and infectious passion for the world around you. Your hugs reminded me everything would be okay as long as I had you. You made every day worth living."

He was crying now too, silent tears streaking down his face. "You are everything to me, and don't you dare think for a second you are foolish. You love fiercely, and you live bravely. You are everything I wanted in a daughter and more."

Adelia started crying again. She had always thought those exact same things about him. How she wished she could be like him one day. How he was her hero. He would always be her hero.

She sniffed, wiping at the tears on her cheeks with her grubby clothes.

"I love you. I love you. *I love you.*" She repeated the mantra. She didn't know how many more times she would ever get to say it. She had to say it enough to make up for a lifetime they would miss.

"I love you more, sunshine. More than you'll ever know."

. . .

THEY HAD FALLEN into a comfortable silence after that. No one had come down to the dungeon since they were thrown down here. Their only company were the rats that scurried around the dank halls. Time was an enigma. No light pierced their dark grave and no meals arrived to mark the passing of time. Her hunger began as a growling companion and grew into a snarling beast. Its protests for food echoed across the dungeon walls so loudly, she almost laughed.

The air was hot and heavy, and sweat built up on her skin like a film. She wished she could take her leg off. The sores and skin irritation were going to be nasty. She was deteriorating from dehydration. It was a slow drain of water from her body and with each passing moment, her soul withered away a little bit more.

She had given up punishing herself for her mistakes. If she were to die, she would do it with no regrets.

She didn't regret trying to save her father.

She didn't regret discovering that she was Fae or had powers.

She had discovered a new world, saw new birds, and made new friends in Maewyn, Rory, and Novak.

She had been able to say goodbye to her dad, something she feared would never happen.

Faerie had been a glimpse of what her life could have looked like, and maybe in the next life she would actually get to live it out.

Despite all its horrors, as her dad said, she saw it for its beauty.

No world was perfect anyway. Not Faerie, not the human world, which she figured she'd never get the chance to go back to anyway. She'd miss her chair on the cliff, her childhood bedroom filled with books. It had been home.

"Hey, Dad, what happened back at the house? Why was there blood all over the floor if you're still alive?"

"The Molten came for me. I don't know how they found me, but they did." He held up his shirt to reveal a massive healing wound across his stomach. It would leave a scar, but she could tell something had been done to speed the healing.

"I managed to escape and get to your uncle Tadriel. He's also Fae, by the way."

She smiled softly to herself. He had no idea she had spent time with him before coming here.

"You have to understand time works differently in Faerie. I got to Tad, he healed me as best he could, and then I decided to go investigate the gate. His familiar Cerla came with me in case anything went wrong and I needed to send a message back to him. I had no idea it would go *that* wrong, though. I went because I needed to figure out if it was just a hole that had formed or if the whole gate was crumbling. I thought I could do it all and get back home before you even finished work. I was going to tell you then—about everything. I knew you weren't going to be safe anymore."

He continued, "But when I got there, I realized the gate was already broken. Molten swarmed me in no time at all. I never even had a chance to fight back. I gave the key to Cerla to take back to the mortal realm to you. I thought it would be safe there. Safer than with Tad in Faerie where the Molten could easily get to him."

That's where he misjudged her. How could he have thought she would sit back and be idle if he went missing?

"You really thought I wouldn't come looking for you?"

He chuckled. "I'm still not sure how you managed to even find out about Faerie, let alone get here. I thought I was playing it safe." He angled an eyebrow at her curiously. "Care to explain?"

"I'm resourceful. I think I get that from you." She had no intention of telling him about Ash. At least not yet. She wanted to talk about *anything* else.

"So time works differently here?" Why hadn't the guards told her that? That seemed like important information.

"Honestly, whoever you were travelling with probably didn't even realize that. Most Fae never leave Faerie, which means they would have no idea that time is different here than the human world."

"I guess that makes sense. Did you have a familiar, Dad?"

He smiled sadly. "Yes, I did."

"Will you tell me about her? Him? They?" She had so many questions for him. It was heart-breaking that she had to ask him here.

He nodded, and she knew it wouldn't be an easy story. "His name was Eyrie. He was a bat falcon."

Adelia gasped. *A bat falcon! Dad had a bat falcon as a familiar?*

She visualized her bird book and how majestic bat falcons were. In the mortal realm, they were native to the tropics. They were powerful aerialists, launching their attacks on prey from conspicuous perches high above. They could reach speeds up to hundreds of kilometers an hour.

They sported a black back, head, and tail of rich dark feathers and a contrasting creamy white throat. Their lower breast and belly were black and white barred with their thighs a rusty orange, making it look like they wore little orange trousers.

They were breathtaking birds. Not that she had ever seen one in person—they were a bucket list bird for her.

"What happened to him?"

"Well, after I used the key, I had no more magic, so the bond was severed. Humans can't have familiars. He would have been like a pet, and I couldn't do that to him. I set him free before I fled with you. I like to imagine he's still soaring the skies of Faerie."

Adelia had to agree, at least Eyrie could be free.

SHE TRIED to ignore the biting pain from the handcuffs around her wrists as they sat in silence in the dungeons. Adelia was beginning to wonder if the Molten would let them wither away down here. Maybe that wouldn't be so bad. At least she'd be next to her dad. Just as she was resigning herself to the thought, she heard footsteps coming down the skinny spiral stairs that led to the dungeon.

She looked up at her dad, who had been dozing in his cell against the bars, and she realized with a jolt that she had completely forgotten something. She had been so caught up in reminiscing and pitying herself that she forgot she still had the key around her neck. The Queen had never searched her for anything more than weapons.

"Dad!" she whispered at him as loud as she dared and began to try and pull the key into her mouth. She latched onto it with her teeth, the metal grating as she tried to tug at it by throwing her head around in every direction. She kept it up until the delicate chain she had placed it on snapped and came free. Holding the key in her mouth, she held it out on her tongue for him to see and shock morphed his face.

She closed her mouth, hiding the key against her cheek when moments later a Molten Guard, in his orange and black uniform, stood before her. He unlocked the door to her cell with his blackened hands and roughly grabbed her chains to haul her up and drag her out of the cell.

"Where are we going?!" she asked, trying to make it seem like she was mumbling so that he didn't notice the key.

"The Queen has requested an audience," he replied gruffly.

Ok, this is it, she thought.

She took a deep breath and tried to channel all her years of drama classes in high school. She purposely tried to make a scene and started screaming and flailing so aggressively that the guard was completely thrown off by her outburst.

"No! I won't go!" she screamed and tried to rip her arms from the guard. She faked a stumble towards her dad's cell, careening towards the ground.

This is going to hurt, she thought miserably, then smashed into the ground. Without her hands to catch herself, she found herself face first on the cold stone floor again.

But that was all she needed. Before the guard hauled her back up, she opened her mouth and let the key slide out onto the floor right in front of her dad's cell.

The guard, visibly angry, and unaware of the stunt she just pulled, dragged her back upright by the hair.

She yelped at the biting pain in her scalp but couldn't help the small smirk that appeared. She just hoped her dad knew what to do with the key. Maybe they could actually get out of here.

So much for withering away to dying in the dungeon, but it was probably foolish of her to think the Molten would have allowed that anyway.

CHAPTER 32

RORY

Rory and Novak slowed as they approached a small grey door that was placed within the black stone volcanic walls. Rin ran in agitated circles in front of the door. They had used Rin to track her scent—thank the Orb for familiars—but he was still visibly rattled. They all were. The group had made their way as quickly as they could, but they had to make several detours due to a few risky close calls with the guards in the hall. They couldn't afford another run-in with the Molten.

As they approached the door, Rory heard screaming coming from inside.

But it wasn't just any scream.

It was a scream that came from the soul. It skipped his ears and pierced straight into his heart. It was the type of scream that would haunt his dreams, reminiscent of a person who lost their mind to the abyss.

He hesitantly peered into the doorway... almost afraid of what he would see. Rory stopped breathing when he saw Maewyn and the woman inside. She had Maewyn strapped to a bed, and the look on Maewyn's face was all the information he needed.

Before he even knew what he was doing, he slammed the door open with such force that the hinges broke, and the metal door hung limply.

The woman emitted a shocked yelp as she turned around. "What are you both doing here?" she asked accusingly.

Right. They were still in Molten Guard uniforms. He took her distraction as a chance to stride toward her before she became the wiser and realized he wasn't planning on being friendly.

He caught a glimpse of Maewyn in his periphery. Her sickening screams had faded when he burst into the room, and now she lay motionless. Her complexion had turned gray and ashy, and her forehead was beaded with sweat.

Rory noticed the woman had an empty syringe in her hand.

"We need to take her with us right now," he growled, pointing at Maewyn.

The woman looked outraged at the suggestion. "You can't have her. You just brought her to me! I need to finish running tests!"

Rory had no idea what the woman had done to Maewyn, but he knew he had never been so angry in his life. He clenched his jaw to steady himself, but he felt as if his blood was turning molten like the lava around the castle. It burned through his veins, consuming him. His fury mounted exponentially until his rage overtook him. All there was now was burning resentment and smoking fury.

There was no coming back from where he was now.

This woman, this *thing*, had dared to touch Maewyn, to cause her pain.

She would die for it.

He reached out and grabbed the woman by her throat, lifting

her up into the air. She choked and sputtered, clawing at his bear-like hands. His grip tightened of its own accord, his desire to crush her windpipe mounting like the anger in his veins.

"What. Did. You. Do. To. Her," he growled.

The woman barked a strangled laugh. "If you don't know, then clearly you aren't who you appear to be." Her wild eyes were alive with excitement, and she reached her own hands out and slammed them into his chest.

He realized his mistake a few seconds too late.

Red hot lava seeped from her fingers, burning his chest as he stumbled backward, letting go of her throat.

"Rory!" Novak screamed from beside him as she blasted him with water to counteract the searing of the lava on his skin.

The pain only added to his fiery rage, his vision turning red. He would kill her with his bare hands right here and now. Not even registering the burns or the puddle of smouldering lava at his feet, he strode forward towards her again, reaching out with his powers to the cold stone floor beneath her feet.

He felt each particle of the floor and began to shift them.

He would open a hole to the pits of Hell and watch her burn for hurting Maewyn.

But before he could, a fist connected with his jaw, pain lancing through his skull.

He looked over at Novak in bewilderment, who was seething. She had her hand at the ready to punch him again.

"Stop acting like a raging child!" she screamed at him.

Then Novak tackled him to the ground as the crazed Molten woman levelled another lava spray at them. The scorching lava spilled onto the floor right where they had been standing. Some of the spray splattered out and hit Novak in the shoulder, burning through her uniform instantly. She ground her teeth in pain and rolled farther away from the lava.

The woman was hissing like a viper, the sickly black veins

bulging out from her forehead. She was strong, much stronger than an average Molten Fae. The forbidden magic had started to chip away at her sanity but fed her strength.

"We need to get information from her! You can't kill her!" Novak yelled over the woman's raging screams due to her failure to hit them with her attack.

They needed to stop her now, or more guards would come to investigate the noise. Then again, Maewyn had been screaming in pain, and no one had come to investigate that.

But Novak was right.

They needed to incapacitate her, not kill her. At least not yet.

Novak sprang to her feet nimbly and formed a protective water bubble around them to give Rory a chance to stand back up.

The woman surged forward, banging on the wall with her fists, attempting to burn away the water with her fire, but the wall held steady. The woman was horrifically strong, the barrier threatening to give in from her barrage of fire.

Novak looked at Rory, an unspoken plan forming between them. They had worked together for years in the Faerie Guard. They knew each other's fighting style, their strengths, and their weaknesses. Sometimes they moved so smoothly around each other, it was like a choreographed dance. Novak would spin in one direction, then Rory would duck under her to launch a surprise attack. Novak also knew he had difficulty controlling his anger sometimes, and its cost was never worth what it earned him. He nodded towards her, and they moved.

The woman barreled into the water wall again, and it shook with the force, but then Novak dropped the barrier abruptly, throwing the woman off. In quick succession, she threw a water cannonball at the woman's face that exploded with a splash. Nothing damaging, just enough to cause her to stumble backward in surprise.

At that moment, Rory lifted the earth from the ground to create a small ledge behind her, and the woman tripped and went sprawling backward. Her head connected with the metal table Maewyn was on with a sickening thud.

Rory lifted more stone into the air, melding the atoms within to create handcuffs made of stone. He brought them down onto her arms and legs, attaching them to the ground.

Breathing heavily, he looked over at Novak, who was holding her shoulder but dropped it abruptly as soon as she noticed his glare. She was injured, which meant their dire need to get out of here was growing more significant.

The Molten woman was now writhing, the sickly black veins on her skin bulging with effort again as she tried to break free from her stone-hewn handcuffs.

Magic was all about imagination.

Your mind is the only barrier to your strength and your creativity is the only barrier to your power.

He took a deep breath and let Novak do the rest. He could think straight enough to know stepping back at this point and letting Novak take over was the best decision.

Novak bent over the woman with a snarl on her lips. "You're going to tell us what you did to our friend, now. Because as you can probably tell, we aren't afraid to kill you. But I think that leaving you alive might be more of a threat anyway. We'll leave you here for your Queen to find. You can tell her you let intruders into your lab to destroy your research and take your prized test subject. I wonder what she would think about that." Novak donned a thoughtful look in mockery.

The woman glared back. "What happens if I tell you, then?"

"All we do is take our friend and leave your precious research. No one but you knows we are even here, so you get away scot-free."

Rory didn't want to agree with that part, but he stayed silent.

Despite the ferocity with which she fought back, the woman was no warrior. It was clear she knew she had the disadvantage now that she was pinned down and had no intentions of dying today.

The woman growled. "Fine," she said through gritted teeth.

"You think that after all these years, we were just waiting behind the gate peacefully? That we weren't planning our revenge? We were *locked* away. Our freedom was *stolen* from us. The Queen knew one day we would be free again, and we would be ready. My team and I have perfected a formula that takes the magic power from one Fae and combines it with that of another. We created this formula to make *super soldiers*. Your friend here is the first to have survived the injection. Now that I have a formula that works, with more time, I could make a serum to inject *her* power into the Molten."

His blood ran cold at the words. He looked over at Maewyn. Soft, delicate Maewyn, lying on the bed like a rag doll. Knowing Novak would handle the rest, he walked over to her and brushed the wet hair from her face. She was even paler than usual if that was even possible.

His hand caressed her cheek and he noticed the usual rosiness had gone. His hand continued along her chin and down to her neck. A wave of relief hit him as he paused at the slow but steady pulse beneath his fingertips.

Although she didn't look like it, Maewyn was still alive.

He watched Novak stand up slowly. She inhaled deeply and threw her arms out, a tidal wave of water exploded around the room.

Beakers and flasks exploded at the force, sending shards of glass flying. Notebooks and journals were drenched beyond repair, the ink on the pages bleeding out into the surrounding water.

Novak looked back at the woman coldly as she attempted to keep her nose above the water as it closed in around her face.

"You said you wouldn't destroy my work!" she screeched, flailing against her bonds.

"I lied."

CHAPTER 33

ASH

Ash sat in his old bedroom, which still looked the same as when he left. At first glance, the room was barren and cold like the rest of the castle, but if you knew where to look, you'd find pieces of who he was hidden around the room. Like the pile of books under his bed and the shiny rocks he collected as a child from around the volcano.

He stared at Atheris as he slithered up and down his arm happily. He got lost in thought watching his shining scales shift with each movement. He was beyond thrilled to have his familiar back again. He had long given up the hope of getting the viper back after the war. Despite this resignation, the hole he had felt in his soul at losing Atheris had never shrunk. According to his mother, they had tried to set the viper free, but Atheris had stayed. It was like the viper knew Ash was still out there and would one day find his way back home.

Not that Ash had ever planned on coming back home.

His father had set out a fortnight before the Queen had declared war on the Wind Court as a last-ditch effort to parlay with the Wind King. He never wanted the war and sought to stop it before it was too late. His mother never noticed he left or that he had taken Ash with him until it was too late.

The Molten Court was a matriarchy, and his father had served as more of a consort to his mother than anything. Despite this, he never held back his thoughts and ideas during the meetings he was allowed to attend. He always spoke his mind and gave advice where needed, and the rest of the Court had respected him.

Eventually even more than their own Queen.

Maybe that was a catalyst for her descent into madness, but he had never known for sure. He only knew that as he aged, her outbursts increased in frequency and intensity. One moment they would share a laugh or an embrace, and the next she would be yelling or screaming at him.

He could handle the occasional outburst, but one particular afternoon he remembered it had gone so much farther than that. They were having a late family dinner to celebrate the coming winter, a reprieve from the sweltering summer that only ever added to the heat in the volcano they called home. Their closest friends had come to join them for their feast, and Queen Karai had donned a beautiful snowy white gown.

It was so unlike the typical gowns she wore, always black as the volcanic stone, that she was the talk of the event. It glittered with white gemstones, and Ash remembered telling her that she looked beautiful because that's what his dad told him to say to her beforehand.

During the feast, a new pretty young maid had delivered the finest wine to the table upon a silver platter. As she was pouring it into his mother's glass, she had tripped and fallen gracelessly, spilling all the wine onto his mother's gown.

Without blinking, his mother had grabbed the dagger she kept at her side and slit the young girl's throat while still sitting at the dinner table.

Ash remembered the blood from her throat spilling onto the gown, blending with the cherry red of the spilled wine. The girl had hit the floor with a sickening thud, her eyes already vacant.

At that point, Ash realized his mother was no longer the woman who raised him. He was afraid of her.

After that outburst, he started noticing the traces of forbidden magic on her skin. He didn't know much about it when he was younger, other than the fact that it was never spoken of or used. But her violent tendencies and outbursts became more frequent, and her once soft, reassuring hands that held him as a child became blackened and charred like her soul.

After witnessing the maid's death, he had nightmares and would often walk the halls of the castle to shake them off. Anyone who caught him would have been concerned that a child his age was wandering around alone, but he never got caught. And he always had Atheris anyway. He would wander past his parents' corridor, only to hear them arguing.

Then, one night as he was padding down floors of the hallways, barefoot as always because the floors were so warm, he noticed his father was also out of his room. He was dressed as if he was leaving, sneaking out in the middle of the night.

Ash remembered his dad stopping when he saw Ash, barefoot and sleepy-eyed with little Atheris trailing beside him. He looked torn but guided him back to his room and packed a bag for him. Ash had left the Molten Court that night with his dad. His dad told him they were going on an important diplomatic mission to the Wind Count.

Looking back, Ash assumed he was afraid to leave him with his mother. Unstable and violent, he was worried for his son's life.

So they had made their way to the Wind Court.

Along the road, Ash overheard some Fae reporting that the

Molten Queen had declared war on the Wind Court. He told his father, and they rode day and night to get to the Wind Court.

Ash still wasn't sure what his father had planned to do that day, or how he planned to stop the fighting, but he never got a chance.

His mother had sent a small wave of soldiers to scope out the Wind Court long before they had left. They had been biding their time in the Blacklore Woods, waiting for word to attack.

The war started while they were making their way down the Wind Court's cobblestone pathways to the floating castle not two kilometres away. Ash had remembered thinking this place was so much more beautiful than the Molten Court.

Why couldn't they have twirling birds instead of snakes or cute, thatched homes painted blue instead of black stone buildings that absorbed all the light that peeked through the clouds?

They heard the commotion begin outside the main city, and his father had tried to pull him into a nearby shop for shelter.

But he was the King of the Molten.

People knew who he was.

As soon as he appeared at the shop window begging to be let in, he was turned away.

He wasn't to be trusted, and now that he was older, Ash didn't really blame them.

After a few frantic moments, he convinced Ash to ask for entry into a small shop by himself.

Any good standing Fae wouldn't leave a child in the streets to die, and luckily no one knew who he was. An older Fae gentleman with mousy brown hair and a large mustache had pulled him inside the store and tried to pull Ash away from the windows.

But Ash had stood there frozen, as his father had valiantly stood his ground in the streets to stop the horde of Molten surging down the streets to the castle.

Ash had been convinced they would stop.

That they would listen to their King.

Whether they were too crazed from the forbidden magic or were never truly loyal to him, he'd never know.

The Queen had given orders, and they followed them.

The bloodlust in those soldiers' eyes was inhuman, and no reasonable argument could have changed the course of those monsters on that fateful day.

Ash had watched from the window of *Otto's Healing Herbs* as his father was mauled by his own army.

They ripped him to shreds for trying to peacefully end the war that was just beginning.

Ash still had night terrors of watching from the window.

In the dreams, he was older, but Otto still held him back as he tried to run outside. He was unable to break from his grasp despite Otto's age and frailty.

Old Otto had taken him in after that day.

Ash had no home to go back to anyway. He was trapped outside the Molten Court and could not return to his mother with the new barrier in place.

Not that Ash had wanted to go back.

He spent the rest of his childhood in that little healing shop with Otto, who had no family of his own.

Otto taught him about the herbs in the shop, how to set a bone, and how to cure a fever. It was so tame compared to the life he had been living before, and for a long time, he relished in the quiet.

Otto advised him to avoid using his magic for fear of persecution.

If the Wind Court found out a Molten was living among them, Ash would be dead. The fear from the war was still too fresh, and eventually, the Fae forgot that there were any innocent Molten at all.

They had all been classified as dangerous, monstrous creatures, and Otto made Ash swear he'd never use it.

And he didn't. For a long time.

But eventually, Ash felt the draw of magic in the air that became too great to ignore.

He began to spend his free time at the border of the Blacklore Woods, away from the Wind Court, to practice his magic.

He relished in the feeling of fire at his fingertips, finally being released after years of suppression.

He had been trying to hide who he was, and until he started practicing magic, he had forgotten what it felt like to be himself.

One particular day while practicing in the forest, he felt a different kind of pull. This type of magic seemed condensed in a certain area; it didn't flow through the air in the same way normal magic did. It was eerie and beautiful, and it called out to him in a way he had never felt before.

Before he knew what was happening, he focused on it and tried to pull the energy away from the source and towards him.

The new magic had flooded his veins, igniting his soul.

It was intoxicating compared to the magic he was used to feeling, and he couldn't stop.

He siphoned the mysterious magic into his blood and felt electrified. The magic was so pure that it made his head spin with the rush of it.

He wanted more.

He hadn't felt this alive since coming to the Wind Court and losing his dad. It woke up a part of his soul that had been slumbering for years, and Ash wanted to feel this magic for the rest of his life.

That was until a young male Fae came stumbling into the clearing and fell to his knees before Ash.

Ash realized far too late that the source of the magic had been *from* this Fae.

He had been stealing his magic away from him.

This was forbidden magic.

Horror overcame him as he rushed to the young Fae to see if he was okay, and he felt a wave of relief to see he hadn't fully drained the young man.

He had only taken enough to weaken him, and the young Fae had probably chalked the bizarre feeling up to being sick.

He'd realize later he was missing a significant portion of his power.

But Ash never told him.

He let the boy walk away after helping him up, still dazed and confused.

Sometimes he blamed Otto for the incident. He had always avoided talking about forbidden magic. He never bothered to teach him about it, so Ash had never known.

But it wasn't until he looked down at his hands and realized they had turned as black as soot, the skin beginning to crackle and peel, that he realized the true weight of what he had just done.

He rushed back to Otto, fearful of the old man's reaction, but not knowing what else to do.

Otto had taken one look at Ash's hands and realized his grave mistake.

He gave Ash a pair of old leather gloves to hide the scars and finally told him about the magic.

How using forbidden magic was to steal the essence of another person, and once you began, the desire to continue was overwhelming.

Ash swore then he'd never use his powers again.

He would never again let himself feel the fire in his veins.

It was too risky.

He extinguished the flames in his soul until he was nothing but smoking embers.

He didn't trust himself to stay in control should he ever reach for magic again.

The pull to use forbidden magic would be too great.

The high was too addicting to avoid.

Ash looked down at his hands now as he sat upon his childhood bed. He detested seeing them, but covering them up while in the Molten Court was blasphemy.

He didn't belong here.

He had to find a way to get himself out.

He had to find a way to get *them* out.

He couldn't leave Adelia in the dungeons to die.

He was running out of time and needed to come up with a plan.

He'd do anything to get her out.

Even use his magic.

There were more important things than his fear and Adelia Larson was one of those things.

CHAPTER 34

Adelia found herself with the Queen of the Molten once again, but Ash was nowhere to be seen this time. *Good.*

The last thing she wanted right now was to see him. She hoped that viper of his accidentally bit him, and he died a slow, painful death.

Adelia was in a smaller room but no less grand than the throne room. Various fountains of lava bubbled from the corners, casting the room in a warm orange glow. It was as hot here as it was in the dungeon, but no one else seemed to mind other than her. Adelia assumed they were all used to it by now, or perhaps even immune to the heat somehow? There had to be some magic to it, like how they used fire magic without burning themselves.

This time the Queen sat upon a smaller cushioned chair, a black stone goblet in her grasp that she swirled and sipped leisurely. Two guards stood on either side of her, avoiding eye contact with Adelia entirely.

The Queen cocked her head like an animal as Adelia walked

in, and then she was roughly pushed to her knees in front of the Queen. She already knew where this was headed; her dad had told her as much in the dungeons. She had already lied to her friends about the location of the key; keeping it from Queen Karai would be simple.

The Queen picked at her long black painted nails before looking up at Adelia. "So, darling. This doesn't have to take long. I'm not cruel, you see. Merely an act I must keep up. "

Adelia almost laughed out loud at the statement. Her father's injuries begged to differ.

"All I need is that little key that I'm sure you know lots about. Your dearest father insists he doesn't have it. So, I will ask you nicely this one time. If you decide not to answer us, then next time I will not be as nice. I'm sure if he were to watch you being beaten as he was, he would be more inclined to talk. But like I said. I'm not that cruel." She smiled then, malice glittering in her dark eyes.

She appeared absolutely feral. It was hard to look at her. The Queen regarded Adelia as if she were a snack, a light meal she could tear apart with her bare hands.

She'd be a fool to think the Queen had any intentions of playing nice.

And Adelia was done with being foolish.

They could torture her here, today, as long as they didn't bring her dad up to watch. She was seriously concerned that he would give up the location if he had to endure watching her get tortured.

"I only came here to free my father from you. I didn't even know Faerie was a place until a few weeks ago. I don't know anything about a key. Unless you mean my car keys, which I sadly don't have here with me." She smiled sweetly back at the Queen, batting her eyelashes innocently.

The Molten Queen could go fall into the lava moat and drown.

There was no way in hell she was giving up the location of the key.

If they found out where it was and destroyed it, then it would all be over. Adelia figured it had taken her dad a lifetime to forge it, and she knew even without asking that he had been selfish for fleeing after he used it. He probably never passed on his knowledge, and if they died here, it would die with him. There would be no way to contain the Molten again and stop another war from breaking out.

She thought maybe, just maybe, if they escaped with the key, they could use it. Imbue it with more magic to re-solidify the gate. But they needed to escape first. She needed to make it through this encounter.

"Do *not* test my patience, girl," Queen Karai gritted out.

She stood up and strode over to where Adelia was kneeling. Her gown today was a dark crimson that sparkled in the flickering light of the lava around them. She roughly grabbed Adelia's chin, forcing her eyes up. Her dark, depthless eyes sent shivers down her spine; they were lifeless, devoid of any emotion, completely soulless. This close to the Queen, unnatural heat radiated from the seeping cracks in her skin.

"I will ask only once more. *Where* is the key?"

Adelia closed her eyes. "I don't know," she said and braced for impact.

The Queen reeled back and hit Adelia across the face. She was knocked off her knees and went sprawling to the ground. Without hands to catch her, her face smashed on the cold stone, rattling her teeth. She could taste the blood in her mouth.

The Queen straightened back up, cold glittering violence written in every line of her lithe body. "Foolish girl. But then again, I should have expected as much. A girl dumb enough to walk into the Molten Court with the Crown Prince and not realize who he was? Now that is laughable. He truly is my son to have tricked you so thoroughly."

The comment stung more than the slap to the face did. Mainly because of the truth that fell heavy in her words. Ash had lied about who he was, not just to her but to all his friends. Adelia still couldn't wrap her head around the fact that he was the son of the woman who had kidnapped her father, of the mad woman who had started this whole war. Ash was cold occasionally but never cruel.

The version of Ash in her mind didn't match with who he truly was.

The Queen motioned to the one guard who had been standing at her side by the throne with impatience. He walked over and held a large metal pole in his charred hands. Adelia racked her brain as to what it could be. Were they planning to hit her with it? As he walked closer, however, she noticed the end of the pole had a round flat disc on it. Her stomach dropped.

Oh God, it's for branding.

The Queen roughly grabbed it from the guard with her burned hands and leaned in closer to Adelia. "This is a little taste of what will come if you don't start talking." She smiled again, feral as a lion.

She lifted her hand to the end of the branding stick and used her own fire and heat to bring the metal to a softly glowing orange. Adelia noticed the end of the pole had the same symbol on it as the key. The Molten Court crest.

The Queen walked around behind her, her blood-red dress scraping across the stone floor. When she had reached Adelia's back, she gently moved Adelia's sweaty hair from the back of her neck and swept it over her shoulder.

That was one small relief; Adelia had always loved her curls, so at least the Queen wasn't planning on balding her.

Adelia took a deep breath in and waited for the pain to come. She was no stranger to the pain of burns after the injuries from the first encounter she had with the Molten. She knew it was fruitless to try and escape at this point; she was handcuffed, starved, and Queen Karai was so powerful, she could easily burn Adelia to ash before she even got three feet away. No, all she could do was try not to pass out and think about getting back to that dungeon, where she hoped her father had caught onto her plan.

Then the Queen brought the pole down onto the back of her neck, below the base of her skull. The brand burned through layer after layer of skin and the pain mounted with each passing second. She was vaguely aware that she was screaming, but her mind was dissociating from her body. Her vision flickered, and images flashed before her eyes as she tried to think of anything but the pain consuming her. She saw her father waiting for her in the dungeon below, pacing in his cell, hoping she would survive this mad excursion. She saw Maewyn, Rory, and Novak waiting for her.

Adelia reminded herself of the people who cared about her, who were counting on her. This was just a little pain, a blip in the road to a better life for all of Faerie.

She lifted her head as Queen Karai finished and locked eyes with her. She silently vowed to stop this woman, *this monster,* who had tried to take everything away from her. She tried to tell her without words that she had messed with the wrong Fae and that she would regret this. She could not be broken, for she was the wind. She was a storm ready to be unleashed, a hurricane waiting just off the coastline for its chance at destruction.

Queen Karai balked slightly at the intensity in her gaze, but replied severely, "You are a lying, filthy Wind Fae. I will destroy you and all of your kind for what you did."

Adelia tried to fake a laugh. "You realize I didn't even know Faerie existed until recently, right? Your feud with the courts doesn't end because you torture me."

"You may be right, but it will give me immense pleasure to cause you pain regardless."

"Just like a Canada Goose," Adelia mumbled.

"What did you say to me?" she snarled back.

"You're like a Canada Goose. They think they're tough. They scare people by flapping their wings and snapping their beaks, but at the end of the day... a goose is still a goose. You can sit here and try to scare me. You can threaten to kill me and break me, but it won't matter. You are nothing but a sad, old woman. You think revenge will make you happy. You are content to bring others down because you've been treated poorly in the past. But you know what? That doesn't make you any better than them. It makes you the Canada Goose of Faerie. Sad, lonely, and desperately trying to prove to the world you're scary. But we see right through you."

Then, a door to the left of the throne opened, and Ash walked in. He froze when he saw Adelia sprawled on the floor, and Adelia could have sworn a wave of glittering cold anger flashed in his eyes.

His jaw ticked almost imperceptibly as he stared at her with his light caramel eyes. He was clean and dressed in an entirely new outfit. Long gone was the Faerie Guard uniform, replaced by a regal black and orange tunic and tight-fitting pants. His red and orange iridescent viper was coiled around his wrist, and it flicked its tongue out every few moments to taste the air around it.

It physically hurt to see him healthy and at ease while she was beaten and broken on the floor. How had she been so blind?

Queen Karai hadn't noticed his entrance; she was still standing over Adelia, seething.

"Mother, I need a word," he stated. Cold fury blazed in her eyes at being interrupted, and she looked as if she was about to tell him she was busy, to come back later.

"*Now*," he added, and Adelia swore the Queen's eyes softened at her son's assertiveness.

"Fine, darling," she said to him and looked back at Adelia. "I will deal with you again later," she hissed, venom coating each word. It was a promise laced with the guarantee of pain and torture.

As she turned to join him, Ash's mask lifted for another fleeting moment, and his mouth moved almost imperceptibly, mouthing silent words at Adelia.

Except she couldn't read what he was trying to say.

He willed her with his eyes to understand but when his mother looked up at him, he glanced away quickly. They strode off together without another look back.

When she was returned to the dungeon, her father jumped to his feet. He searched her for signs of injury, his eyes falling on her swollen lip, purpling jaw and the way she gingerly held her shoulders.

After the guard left, she noticed he dropped his hands to his sides, and she realized he had been faking holding them behind his back.

A slow, mischievous grin broke out on his face.

"You ready to get out of here, sunshine?"

Moments later, they both stood outside their cells, hands finally free of the biting handcuffs. It was such a relief, Adelia could have cried. She reached up to touch the brand on her back and winced. She deftly braided her hair to the side to avoid the sticky strands getting caught in the freshly wounded skin.

Teilio reached out to pull Adelia into a bone-crushing hug before they set out. She breathed in his scent and she was home.

He stroked her hair a few times silently, no more words needed to be said. It had felt like their last hug was a lifetime ago, and she didn't realize how much she feared never being able to do so again.

But they were here, they were alive, and they would survive.

They broke apart and her father was shaking his head in disbelief. "I still can't believe you put the key on a necklace and started wearing it around. I really thought you'd keep the key safe, not wear it as jewelry and come sauntering into the *one* place you most certainly should have avoided."

He laughed, staring at his hands in awe.

When she had returned to the dungeon to find her father handcuff free and saw his exuberance, she knew he had done precisely what she had planned. The gate had already failed, so Teilio had taken back his magic. Her father had been able to break the locks on the handcuffs and cell doors with a little bit of wind pressure. He already looked lighter and healthier than she had ever seen him in her life. The key had taken so much from him, but the gate had failed, so he had taken his power back.

When they were out of here, they would figure out what to do about the key. How to imbue it with the proper amount of magic to seal the Molten away forever.

To seal Ash away forever, she thought.

But she couldn't dwell on that. After the horror and destruction the Molten had laid upon the Wind Court last time, they couldn't waste any more time. They needed to reseal the gate and stop the power-hungry Queen Karai from killing hundreds of Fae again.

Now that her hands were free, she could feel the magic thrumming and knew they actually stood a chance of escaping.

She knew they stood a better chance if they had a plan, but she had no idea how long they had been down here or where the rest of the team was. Novak, Maewyn, and Rory could be dead for all she knew. They would have to take things one step at a time and work their way through this volcanic maze until they found an exit. She hoped their magic would be enough of a weapon.

Her dad gave her a silent nod, ensuring she was ready to go. She nodded back, and they moved towards the stairs descending into the dungeon. That was when they heard someone coming down the steps, the gentle footsteps growing louder and louder.

Oh God, not now.

The chances of being caught were increasing with every moment they waited.

Adelia looked at her dad for an idea. To her, it only sounded like one person. They both had their powers back and could probably take on one Molten, as long it was just a guard.

But if it was the Queen, then they would be in trouble.

Her dad's eyes glinted with excitement. She could only imagine what he was feeling after getting his power back after decades. He took a fighting stance, and despite his ripped and tattered clothes and his weaning physique from weeks of starvation and torture, he looked like a soldier.

He had fought in a war and survived before; this was nothing.

Adelia had done her part. She had gotten him out, returned his powers, and now it was his turn.

They weren't going back into their cells to hide.

It was their time to fight.

Adelia knew this would be their only chance to escape, to use the key and stop the Molten.

She looked over at him, and all she saw was love.

His eyes sent radiating beams of faith piercing into her heart. It flooded her system, ran through her veins, and shone outward. Their love for each other, as father and daughter, was an incandescent light. With that light she purged the dark fear that had been festering in her soul and made room for love.

She made room to hope again.

Hope and love would purify the dark thoughts that plagued her conscience. She'd never been foolish. She was headstrong and cared for the people around her fiercely.

She didn't need anyone to put her broken pieces together again.

She could do that herself.

She copied his stance and prepared to use her powers along with his. She felt it with every fibre of her being, from her pounding heart down to her fingertips. She reached out into the air for the magic around her and the stale air of the dungeon was ready to come to her call.

She was ready.

She was ready to fight for her life.

Fight for her father.

Fight for their future.

That was, until Ash stepped around the corner.

CHAPTER 35

MAEWYN

Maewyn woke to a hard pressure on her back. It was digging into her spine right above her hips, making her want to shift positions. She went to roll over and go back to her carefree, dreamless sleep, but her body screamed in agony when she tried to move.

Everything came rushing back in.

The woman in the lab coat.

The injection.

The pain.

Bile rose in her throat at the sureness she had felt back in the lab, the sureness that she would die. But she definitely wasn't dead.

Still lying on her back, she opened her eyes to see a soft canopy of trees overhead, dancing in the gentle wind. She realized that it was a rock underneath her back because the ground she was lying on was uneven and bumpy.

The soft, reassuring texture of Rin's coat against her leg let her know he was lying beside her.

She must have been removed from the lab.

Struggling to rise with a groan, she saw Rory and Novak sitting close by around a small fire. It wasn't nighttime, so they appeared to be using the fire to cook something.

"Hey," she said weakly, her own voice unrecognizable. It was scratchy and raw. She remembered screaming endlessly back in the lab, unable to control the cries that ripped out from her after the injection.

What had that lady done to her anyway?

She wiggled her toes and flexed her fingers tentatively.

She didn't *feel* any different.

She felt incredibly sore, like she had fallen off The Perch in the Wind Court—from the very top floor—but otherwise normal.

Rory and Novak looked up at her meek voice, dropped their skewers, and came rushing over to kneel beside her. Rory looked like he hadn't slept in days. The dark shadows beneath his eyes were cavernous, and his ordinarily silky black hair was dishevelled and dirty. He bent down, feeling her forehead with the back of his hand tenderly, visibly relieved at her lack of fever.

"How... how are you feeling?" he asked her gingerly.

Her first instinct was to say sore, but with each moment she was awake, it ebbed away.

She felt like she had newfound energy.

There was a fire in her veins that willed her to get up off this sodden forest floor and move. It was a weird feeling, like she had twice as much blood pumping through her veins, supplying her muscles with twice as much oxygen. Even as she sat and contemplated how she was feeling, the soreness dispersed.

"Good? I don't know why, but I feel good." She lifted her pale hands to her face to inspect them for something amiss but discovered nothing.

She moved to stand up, but Rory's strong hand came down on her shoulder to hold her still for a moment longer.

He appeared concerned like he was worried she might sprout horns or a tail at any moment.

"Rory, I'm actually okay. In fact, I think I'm better than okay. I feel like I could get up now and storm back into the castle and take on twenty guards myself. I feel *alive*." She was confused as she said it, but it rang true. Her energy was increasing with each moment she was awake, the entropy of her atoms in her blood climbing.

Rory still didn't speak, and she looked at Novak in concern. She wore a similar expression to Rory's.

"What?" Maewyn asked. "Why are you both looking at me like that?"

"Here," Novak said and passed her a dagger.

Confused, Maewyn stared at the dagger. "Um, thanks? But I don't need another dagger. I have my own weapons." She went to hand it back.

But Novak shook her head and pushed it back to her. "Use the reflection. Look at your eyes, Maewyn."

Maewyn complied.

She brought the shining dagger to her face. Her reflection stared back at her in the polished silver. She took in her stark white hair and normally icy blue eyes, except her eyes weren't blue anymore.

They were the colour of molten ore.

They were a swirling kaleidoscope of reds, oranges, and yellows that seemed to flicker in the afternoon sun.

She yelped and dropped the dagger, and pure panic seized her chest.

What had that lady done to her?

What had she become?

She had always had her mother's eyes, and before today,

anytime she looked in the mirror, it was like her mother was there staring back.

Like her mother had never really left her.

But not anymore.

Looking up at her friends, tears welled in her eyes.

Rory, without speaking—because sometimes there was nothing to say—reached over to her and enveloped her in one of his warm hugs.

Except his hug didn't feel warm anymore. She was the warm one now. She had literal fire in her veins.

She nuzzled into him, silently letting the tears fall.

AFTER SHE HAD COMPOSED HERSELF, Novak began to tell her what the lady in the lab had told them. Novak didn't mention the woman's fate, and Maewyn thought maybe it was better if she didn't know.

After Novak told her the woman had infused Maewyn with a serum to make her a super soldier, she had stopped listening.

She couldn't wrap her head around the fact that she might have more powers. The woman had obviously only intended to use Maewyn as a test subject and not to actually let her live if it worked. But here she was—the first Fae with more than one court's power.

She was afraid to try and reach out with her magic. To find that it wasn't true and that she had instead lost her connection to her ice and snow. However, deep down, she knew it wasn't true because the energy coursing through her right now was more potent than ever in her life. Her skin was buzzing, and the magic in the air was calling out to her.

Did that mean she could create fire like the Molten?

She wanted to try, but for some reason, she wanted to do it without the company of her friends. They showed such concern and worry for her that if she started creating dancing sparks from her fingertips, they might faint.

All that really mattered right now was that they came for her.

Rory came for her.

She decided to change the subject for now and move on. "Novak? Where are Ash and Adelia…?" she wondered out loud.

Both her friends paled at the question.

"We don't know," Novak replied bitterly.

Novak always had the answers to everything.

"What do you mean you don't know?"

"After we saved you, we had to get out of the castle. The halls were still empty and you were unconscious and burning up. We thought you were going to die, Maewyn. I had to rely on Ash and Adelia to get Teilio and get out to safety without us."

"And?" Maewyn asked.

"That was days ago."

Her jaw dropped.

Days? She had been unconscious for days?

Rory replied this time, "Novak was hurt during the fight too, and with you unconscious, there was nothing we could do. It would have been suicide to go back in. We hoped they had just run into some trouble but would figure it out. Those two are intuitive."

"Well, I'm awake now. We can't wait any longer. No one gets left behind. Let's go get our friends."

CHAPTER 36

 Ash looked genuinely surprised to see Adelia and Teilio standing outside their cells, ready to attack. He looked at both of them, an amused grin tugging at his lips.

"I assume you are both ready to go? Adelia, as eager as ever."

He leaned back against the cold stone wall behind him, arms crossed, and Adelia didn't stop to think as she threw her power at his chest. She *needed* to wipe that arrogant grin off his face.

His stupid, lying, traitorous face.

She knocked the breath from him with the force of her power and held him there, pinned to the wall with the effort of her wind.

"How *dare* you come down here acting like you did nothing wrong. Like you have any right to talk to me after leaving me here to die."

"It's okay, Goldilocks. I'm here to help you escape."

"You're a bit late," she seethed at him.

"I see that. You've always been competent on your own. You

keep proving that to me over and over again." He sounded genuinely impressed.

"You foul viper," she spat.

"Actually, that's Atheris, and he doesn't like it when you call him foul." At that, the small iridescent snake poked its head out from his breast pocket quickly enough that it shocked Adelia into dropping the wind that held Ash pinned.

"Get out of here, Ash. Go running back to your mommy. I'm sure she's so happy to have her beloved son home to help her *murder* all my people."

His eyes thinned at that. She thought she detected that cold anger again at the mention of his mother, but he didn't comment. Instead, he replied, "Actually, I'm coming with you."

"*Ha!* No, you aren't."

She couldn't believe him.

He had the audacity to lie to her.

To leave her in the dungeon to die, then show up and assume they would escape together, off into the sunset?

"Get out of our way, Ash. Don't make me hurt you."

His eyes gleamed with the challenge. Like he wanted her to try, to see what could happen. Then she remembered he had the same powers as the Molten that attacked her house. He had fire and lava at the tips of his fingers.

She couldn't stop her gaze from moving to his hands.

His blackened, scarred hands he had hidden from her.

He was a force with his sword alone, but now that she knew he had powers too, he was so much more deadly than she had realized.

"Then attack me, Adelia."

She growled back.

She didn't have *time* for this. They needed to get out of here *now*.

She looked back at her dad, who was standing there bewildered. He had been there when Ash was revealed to be the Crown Prince in the throne room, but how much did he remember? She wasn't sure if he knew they *were* friends at one time, or if all he saw was the enemy.

"Can you give us a minute, Dad?"

He was growing more confused by the minute, but conceded and moved towards the stairs. "You've got a couple minutes. I'll keep watch in case anyone else comes this way." He eyed Ash suspiciously. "You sure you're okay, sunshine?"

She nodded.

Her dad moved away, leaving Ash and Adelia alone in the barren dungeon.

Ash moved to step closer to her, but she slammed her hands into his chest and shoved him.

Hard.

"You tricked me!" she yelled as loud as she dared while still in the dungeons. "You are a damn Molten Prince! I trusted you, Ash. I trusted you." She tried to keep her voice from breaking, from giving away how hurt she was.

"I'm here now, aren't I?" He smirked at her. "I told you to trust me, Adelia. I told you I wouldn't leave you. And I keep my promises."

God, his smirk was infuriating.

"Is that so? What about the past few days, when I've been down here being tortured and starved, and you've been living in luxury up there? You made no move to help me then. You don't get to decide when being a hero suits you best."

He finally dropped his smirk. "You have *no* idea what it is like up there, Adelia."

"Then enlighten me, please! I'm hanging on your every word, *Your Highness*."

"None of that is even important right now. All that matters

is that you're here, you're alive. Oh, and also that you are beautiful, and I really should have told you that before."

Her mouth dropped open, and he stared into her eyes like he was staring into her soul.

"I wanted you to know that. I couldn't stop thinking about you every moment I was up there with *her*. I'm *glad* you were down here in the dungeon most of the time. It was probably safer."

She was incredulous, but her traitorous heart still skipped a beat at his words.

"I know you don't want to believe me, but I hated being up there. I broke when I saw you bleeding on the floor in front of my mother, but I had to figure out a plan to get us out safely. I needed them to trust me if I had any hope of exploring the castle to find a way out. I needed to come down here to get you without being watched."

She didn't even have words for him.

Her thoughts were muddled, trying to sort out how she should feel about him. She was angry, *so angry*, but he had stepped closer to her again tentatively, and she felt her body betraying her.

Heat rolled off of him, his breath on her skin.

His lips were so close to hers—those horrible, lying, traitorous, *full* lips.

He lifted his hands up to her face, cupping it beneath his palms. She expected his hands to feel dry and scaly, but they just felt warm on her face. "I know I have so much to explain to you. But I promise you, I was never going to leave you here to die. I am not my mother. I am a Faerie Guard. I took an oath, Adelia. And I will take another oath right here, right now." His thumb idly stroked her cheek, lightly brushing her bottom lip and sending shivers down her spine. The warmth was back in his caramel eyes, and he was looking at her with awe.

When she had met him, she had thought he had been hard to read, but now she realized the emotions in his eyes told stories.

His eyes conveyed the thoughts and words he never said.

They showed the colours of his soul.

His hands may be black and burned, evidence that he had lived through dark times, but his eyes were a kaleidoscope of bright hope.

She knew looking at him that his words rang true. He had lied, yes, but he had never abandoned her. And she had to remember that she had lied to him too.

If she hadn't convinced them to come here on her reckless mission, he likely would have never come back, prince or not.

"Adelia, I want you to know you can trust me. I vow to never keep another secret from you as long as I live. I have just been so fucking ashamed of where I came from and who I am that I never wanted anyone to find out. I was naive to think I could keep this a secret. I thought it was the best way to keep everyone safe. But I was so incredibly wrong. All I can do now is try and make up for everything. I'll do my best to keep you safe while you save the world." He smirked, his eyes sincere but amused. "I will catch you when you trip and support you in all your foolhardy adventures because most of the time, they turn out to be brilliant anyways. I wouldn't dare to underestimate you again."

"It's going to take a lot of sucking up to make up for this," she whispered to him.

He flashed her his signature smirk and poked her nose gently. "I'll spend forever trying to prove to you I'm worthy of you. You're worth it, Adelia. You came in like a blazing sun to brighten up my life. I'm not giving you up that easily."

She saw in his eyes how much he wanted her, and she realized she wanted him too. Despite the lies, she still cared for him.

She wasn't ready to give up on him, *on them*. He had captivated her.

Her breath hitched as he leaned down, his lips brushing hers like a feather.

It felt like a promise.

She wanted more.

She lifted her own hands up to lace them through his smoky grey hair and pulled him closer to her, to feel him against her, when she heard a pointed cough from the doorway.

She bolted away from Ash to find her father standing in the doorway, looking sheepish. He cleared his throat awkwardly.

"I... uh... hate to interrupt, but we are in the dungeon attempting to escape from the Molten Queen. We should probably go..."

Colour rose to her cheeks, whereas Ash gave his best smile, bowing his head toward her father. "Of course, sir, just figured I should say sorry to your daughter." He smirked mischievously down at Adelia and her cheeks reddened further.

That was *not* the type of apology she wanted her father witnessing, nor the kind he would likely approve of.

Her dad eyed Ash with suspicion and gestured for him to go first. Ash sauntered ahead, winking at Adelia as he looked back. Her father pointedly stepped in front of Adelia to separate the two.

CHAPTER 37

As they summited the stairs of the dungeon, finally free of the suffocating heat and the claustrophobic walls, she looked over to see another person leaning casually against the wall at the entrance to the stairs.

It was the prisoner she had freed from the dungeon, the one who had led them right to the trap that had gotten her locked up in this place.

She moved her hands to attack and felt Ash grab her wrist to hold her back.

With a visible sigh, he said, "Adelia, this is Dax."

Confusion flooded her thoughts.

"Dax? Like..." She trailed off and recalled the story Rory had told her while they had been training. The story of the other member of their team who had been a Molten sympathizer.

The member who had ditched them, spoken traitorously of his own King, and come to petition the Molten Court for entry.

"Yeah, that Dax." Ash sounded less than impressed at their new companion.

Dax came over to Adelia, grabbed her hand, and kissed it.

"Pleasure to meet you, beautiful," he purred, and his eyes sparkled with mischief. "Formally, at least."

He had cleaned up since Adelia saw him last. His skin was free from ash and dirt. He had a warm honey complexion despite the lack of sun in the volcano. His hair was indeed a deep chocolate brown, contrasting his piercing blue eyes.

He was incredibly handsome.

Ash bent down to whisper in her ear, "I'd be careful around him, Adelia. His allegiances change with the wind. He's a weak man and untrustworthy, but for now, our goals align."

Dax sauntered over to Ash, clapping him on the back. "Now, don't go filling her head with lies. We all know you've had your fair share of mistakes as well. Or, does she trust you implicitly because she's fallen for your eyes and seductive smirk?" He grinned. "They certainly worked on me." He winked at Adelia and flicked Ash's nose carelessly.

Ash growled.

"Hold up. He literally betrayed us as soon as we let him out of jail. Why trust him now?" she asked incredulously.

She had always thought she was the foolish one, especially after releasing Dax from the dungeon earlier, but now Ash was making the same mistake?

He must have a solid reason for bringing Dax into the equation.

Dax spoke, "I've been in the Molten Court for a year now. Imagine my surprise when I found out my dear friend Ash was Prince Ash of the Molten Fae. So, when you both arrived in front of my cell, I wanted to have a little fun. I kept my promise to bring you to your dad, thus ensuring my escape, and I knew Ash would find a way to get you out. I could tell by the way he looked at you. And I also knew the Queen wouldn't kill you or him. She's cruel, but not *that* cruel."

T.L. WILSON

Adelia thought it seemed odd that the Queen had referred to herself in the same way.

"Didn't she have you thrown in the dungeon...?"

This boy was very confusing. Ash was right. He jumped all over the place like he was surfing on the wind currents.

"Well, yes, but to be fair, I kept seducing her personal guards. She got quite angry when they kept missing their shifts." He winked at Adelia conspiratorially.

Now she was indeed speechless.

"Wait, so you weren't a prisoner here the whole time?"

He laughed at her. "Hell no. Ash here detests what his mother has become because of this war, and I don't blame him. She's certainly not as innocent as I initially thought, but she's not the *real* bad guy."

"What do you mean she's not the real bad guy?"

He smiled conspiratorially again. "Now that's a story for another day. Aren't you anxious to get out of here? Because I know I am. I'm tired of this place. I'm ready to leave."

Adelia's head swam with endless questions from his cryptic responses. The Queen had shown her just how cruel she was today. The brand on her neck pulsed angrily. Adelia couldn't believe there was someone worse than the Queen. She shivered at the thought.

However, he was right, now wasn't the time to bombard him with questions. She trusted Ash, and if he thought Dax was essential to their escape, then she had to go with it.

She was having a hard time disliking him anyway.

There was something intriguing about him. She had a feeling there was a lot more to him. He also clearly got on Ash's nerves, something she could get on board with.

She mentally catalogued Ash's angry reaction after being flicked on the nose for later.

. . .

290

Ash briefly explained his plan. The castle had underground rivers flowing beneath it. He knew they were accessible from the kitchens, so that's where they were headed.

He said the river system was similar to a sewer system; it would take them outside. They all knew walking out the front door again would be impossible. The Queen was on high alert now, and they were preparing to leave for war.

The grounds were crawling with guards too.

It had been sheer luck they got in the first time. Not that it had gone that well anyway, but still, they couldn't risk it again.

The kitchens had access to the tunnels because apparently, they used a small area of the underground tunnels as a warming room, where food waited before large feasts. Ash said the tunnels weren't usually used for anything other than that, so they shouldn't be patrolled.

Apparently, most people didn't even know they existed, but Adelia had a hard time believing that.

She was beginning to realize that things never worked out exactly how she planned, and she had to be ready for it.

She was learning the difference between unrealistic optimism and having hope. Her hope was rooted in pragmatism, in a belief that she would endure and, in the end, work towards a tomorrow that shone a little brighter. She saw the sun on the horizon and knew she had to crawl through the shadows to get there, but she would emerge stronger, brighter, and fiercer.

Her hope filled her with light, and as Adelia looked at the people around her, she saw it reflected in their eyes.

Their journey may be filled with darkness, but they would emerge radiant.

CHAPTER 38

ASH

As they walked in heavy silence towards the kitchen, slinking through the desolate halls, Ash couldn't help but reflect on the bizarre nature of having Dax as company again.

His fellow guard had grated on his nerves even when they had worked together.

His fake charm was nauseating to endure.

Ash could recall one mission where they had been dispatched to the Terrain Court to deal with a Wyvern wreaking havoc on a rural mining village.

They wandered through the village, asking for information on the creature's last known whereabouts before heading into the nearby mountains to hunt it. Dax had instead stumbled upon 'a magnificent creature' in the town. Which meant a young local miner with eyes the colour of the sea that 'hypnotized him.' He told them he wanted to 'find out more about the boy' and he would catch up with them.

Ash and the others had gone on without him, thinking that

Dax had wanted to find out where the dreamy-eyed boy lived, so he could find him later.

But Dax never joined them.

He had left them to deal with the Wyvern themselves, taking the day to indulge in himself instead. They had come back bruised and limping. Even Maewyn was furious at him, and she rarely ever got mad.

That's how it had always been with Dax. He was constantly seeking instant gratification, which meant shirking his responsibilities for a cold drink in a busy local tavern or an interesting conversation with an intriguing stranger.

Ash had thought for sure Dax would have given him away when he and Adelia discovered him in the dungeons, if for no reason other than his own amusement. Instead, he had kept silent, much to Ash's relief at the time, only to realize a few moments later that he had led them right to his mother. There was no way he could have predicted she would be awake that late or in the throne room.

Dax wanted to stir the pot and banked on Ash figuring it out.

He wasn't sure whether to be angry or flattered.

Ash had surprised Dax with a preposition that first night he found him in the castle; help them escape, and Ash would help him gather information on the Wind King. Dax was convinced the Wind King was at fault for the war and deep down Ash knew there had been more to the conflict than what he was told as a child. He just never thought it was his fight.

The King had secrets; he knew that much. He had known that since the war began. He always assumed there was more to it than his mother's greed. Unfortunately, anyone who got close to the truth went missing.

A powerful man like the King had his way of keeping things

hidden, and until now, Ash hadn't cared enough to uncover the truth.

He had been content working for the guard, using his blade as a means of release when he couldn't use his magic. He felt like he was making enough of a difference in the world that way. But after meeting Adelia, Ash knew his time for complacency was over. Adelia lived with so much passion and determination for doing the right thing and he couldn't justify being idle anymore.

When his mother was locked away, the threat of her insanity was not an issue or threat to the rest of Faerie, and that was all that mattered.

But not anymore.

His mother was not the Fae she used to be. She had lost touch with reality during the war and had let her anger and greed consume her. Maybe it started when she began experimenting with forbidden magic, or perhaps it progressed when she thought both he and his dad had died in the war. Either way, he knew there was no coming back from where she was now.

She had changed, and it was too late to pull her back up from the abyss of madness she'd fallen into.

She was already gone.

He would do whatever he needed to do to stop his mother and then help Dax find out why this all began. He'd carry out his father's dying wish; to cull the violence and war and have all the Fae courts living harmoniously.

He would find out what King Orodani of the Wind Court had planned. Find out if he had targeted the Molten in the first place and if he forced his mother to take such desperate measures.

Find out what actually led her to start a war.

Ash would do this for the mother he remembered from his

childhood, the caring woman who wouldn't want her people to die.

For the woman who once cared about her people.

He would do this for his father.

And he would do it for Adelia, who wanted to live in a better world.

DAX ACCEPTED Ash's proposed plan immediately after he explained it to him. He wasn't sure what Dax's motivations were for digging into the mystery of King Orodani, but their goals aligned for now.

Dax would aid in their escape and travel with them. From there, he and Ash would make a plan for obtaining information on the Wind Court. Dax was aloof and selfish, but he wasn't stupid. He knew he couldn't tackle the mystery of the King Orodani alone, and they had all refused him the first time he had asked.

The Queen was unhappy when Ash freed Dax, but she conceded when Ash addressed their long history and friendship.

As much as Ash detested the woman, there were times when the mother she had been before shone through. It served as a heartbreaking reminder of who she once was.

He and Dax had wandered through the halls of the castle 'catching up' but, in reality, had crept down to the kitchens to investigate the old tunnels there. Ash knew it would be suspicious if he went down alone. Even when he was a child, he never spent time in the kitchens. His favourite place had always been the barracks and the training rooms.

That night's ridiculous events came rushing back to Ash.

Once they were down in the kitchens, Dax had served as a distraction to the kitchen staff. Feigning drunkenness, he stumbled into the kitchen, claiming he was looking for more whiskey. It wasn't an unreasonable thing. Anyone who knew Dax would know he enjoyed it a little too much at times.

"What in Faerie are you doing down here, you hooligan?" the unreasonable old head chef barked at him. "Get out of here!"

"Whiskey, my dear lady! Help a fellow out?" he slurred.

"Nice try, boy. I won't ask again. You aren't allowed down here!" She put her hands on her plump hips and waited for him to take his leave, but instead Dax jumped up onto the nearest table.

He stumbled and sent plates of cured meats and cheeses flying across the room. A piece of salami slapped a young fae in the face, and she looked positively scandalized. Once he had his balance, he stood up and began to sing.

"There once was a maiden named Chloe.
Who met a young lad named Joey.
She fell for muscles like rocks
And gargantuan co—"

"Hold up, young man! Stop right there!" She ran over to him, bewildered at his vulgarity, but Dax was only getting started.

He bent down and grabbed the nearest rolling pin and began to dance across the counter. He kicked at the plates and glasses of wine in a spectacular show of complete idiocy. Only Dax could pull this off, and Ash had to admit he was an excellent vocalist.

Unfortunately, Ash was convinced he would get thrown in the dungeon again for it.

As Ash used the distraction to creep past the bewildered kitchen staff, he couldn't help but stifle a laugh at the visibly pink blush across salami girl's face. Try as she might, she couldn't keep her eyes off Dax as he ripped his shirt off and trailed across the counters, showing every bit of his chiselled physique.

She was smitten.

Maybe if Dax had truly been drunk, she'd be safe from his advances, but he was sober as a rock and *definitely* noticed her eyes on him.

In the ensuing chaos, Ash made it to the small door to the warming rooms. He hoped they were still in use and accessible. He was banking on the hope that they hadn't discovered a less crude method for keeping food warm in the years since he had lived here.

He couldn't take the risk of coming down here without checking, not once he had freed Adelia.

Adelia.

He couldn't stand the thought of her being down in the dungeons alone or the look of hatred burning in her eyes when she had seen him earlier. But she had every right to hate him.

He had lied to her—to Maewyn, Novak, and Rory. None of them had known his true identity. Sometimes he had even forgotten, it had been so easy to move on with his life knowing his mother was locked away and he would never see her or any other Molten again.

He couldn't believe he had been so dumb in thinking they could come here, get her dad, and get out without anything going wrong.

Without her finding out who he truly was.

He had tried for years to bury this part of him, to forget where he came from. He wanted so desperately not to become her. He never wanted to give in to the temptation of using forbidden magic again, and *God* was the temptation a weight on his chest every day.

He had almost incinerated his mother and every guard in that room when he walked in today and saw Adelia on the floor. For the first time in years, he had felt the fire on his fingertips, ready to be unleashed in anger. It had been so close... but that wouldn't have gotten them any closer to escaping. He would have been locked up too.

He owed it to Adelia to show more control, and so far, he had managed to avoid using his powers since being back but knew that as soon as he unleashed them and opened the floodgates, he would not be able to hold back. It would be a slaughter, and he knew he would feel no remorse at all... and that's what worried him the most. He'd become whoever he needed to be to get Adelia out.

She was the light to his dark, and he'd tear the world apart to be with her again.

He needed more time with her.

He didn't deserve it, but God, he would try.

He had been trying since he joined the Faerie Guard to make up for the pain, destruction, and death the Molten had caused, but he felt as though nothing he ever did could erase it.

But maybe if he could do something for Adelia, get her and her dad out, then perhaps he'd be okay if she continued to hate him. At least he would have done something of worth. Then he would throw himself into this Wind King mystery with Dax and start fixing both the world and himself.

Maybe one day he'd be worthy of her.

Now, as the unlikely group made their way through the still halls of his childhood home, he felt like an intruder. He led the way, Dax trailing softly behind him, light-footed in a way that only the Wind Fae were. Behind him followed Teilio, who was unnervingly similar in appearance to his daughter the more Ash looked at him. He had bright hazel eyes and honey-blond hair. The only difference was he wore a solemn look of skepticism, whereas Adelia always seemed eager.

He hoped the kitchen would be quiet at this time of night, but that wasn't a guarantee.

His mother's propensity for unpredictability was unrivalled.

Ash eased the door to the kitchen open, peering inside.

It was empty.

Motioning to the others, he opened the door all the way, and the four of them crept in. Clean pots and pans were stacked in the sink, left to drip dry overnight, and the small hearth to the left was unlit. At this time of night, the usual aroma of cooking bread or simmering soup was absent, leaving the room eerily silent—that was... until they heard a small sniffle from the corner.

Ash froze where he stood, the others following suit, afraid to take another step.

Just then, the rosy-cheeked girl that had blushed at Dax's little stunt in the kitchen rounded the corner. Her eyes were puffy, wet tears kissing her cheeks.

She hadn't noticed them yet, and Ash quickly motioned for them all to drop and hide behind the large kitchen island they were standing behind.

Adelia and Teilio followed, but Dax remained standing. Adelia tried to grab his arm and pull him down, but he grinned down at Ash mischievously.

Oh God, what is he planning?

He coughed pointedly, and the girl looked up, surprised, jolted from her thoughts at the sudden noise. Leaving them hidden behind the counter, he approached the girl like a frightened animal.

"Oh, sorry to scare you, beautiful." He flashed one of his smiles dripping with charm. The type of smile that probably made her heart skip a beat because Dax was looking at her as though she was the most beautiful girl in the world. "I was down here looking for a midnight snack."

He reached out to touch her face and gently brush some of the tears from her cheeks.

"What's got you down? I hope it's not some boy." He gently brushed a tear away with his thumb and bent down to kiss the spot where it had been.

She was visibly shaken at the sudden turn of events, but Dax was living for it. Ash could see how much he was enjoying this and how the blush had returned to the girl's fair cheeks.

"No, no, not a boy. Just... just some family stuff," she whispered back, unable to take her eyes from his. She was mesmerized with the intensity of his gaze, and taken aback by his concern for her well-being.

"Ahh, I see." He dropped his hands to her shoulders and began idly stroking her collarbones and along her neck. Then Ash watched as he spun her around and began to massage her shoulders.

"How about I help with some of this stress then?" Dax leaned a little closer to her ear as he continued to massage her shoulders. "I know a few other ways that could help too." He nipped playfully at her ear.

That was all he needed. The girl was utterly smitten. A handsome young boy, the cover of darkness, and she was thoroughly distracted, well enough for them to slip by unnoticed now.

That poor girl.

She was doomed.

He glanced over at Adelia crouched beside him, with her inquisitive hazel eyes and blond curls crashing in waves around her shoulders.

But then again, so was he.

CHAPTER 39

Adelia waited for Ash to give the all-clear, as Dax kept the young girl thoroughly distracted. He motioned for Adelia and Teilio to follow him, and they dipped out from behind the counter, running in crouched positions over to the warming room door.

They eased inside, and before the door fell shut, she heard Dax say, "I'll meet you upstairs soon." Then he joined them in the dim light.

Adelia gave him an incredulous look, to which he shrugged and pulled the door shut.

They were plunged into warm darkness. The blackness engulfed them all, and they were blind. Adelia tried to hold her hands up to her face and couldn't even see their silhouettes.

She had never been afraid of the dark growing up and found solace in it sometimes. The early morning was also the best time to birdwatch, and she couldn't count how many times she had risen before the sun to wander out into the woods with her binoculars in the waning dark.

This dark was different, though.

She knew she was trapped in a volcano deep below the earth, no whisper of moonlight or stars to brighten their path. She tried to steady her breathing and shake off the eerie feeling that plagued her.

She wished Ash would use his powers and give them some light, but he had been so hesitant to use them. She wasn't sure why, it would certainly be easier, but now wasn't the time to ask.

Ash's warm voice was the first to echo through the darkness. "Hold up, I have to find the bag I left here," he whispered to no one in particular, and Adelia could hear him begin to shuffle around in the dark to search.

"I left a bag down here earlier, with a few things we might need. Matches, a lantern. Stuff like that."

She waited for him to search around, wanting to help but also having no idea where her own feet were. Seconds later, his hard body bumped into hers, and she stumbled in the dark.

The force from his shoulder caused her to trip on the uneven ground and spiral towards the ground.

Her first thought was, *oh God, not again.* She had fallen so many times already since being here. Her face was already littered with bruises.

Then his strong hands caught her, righting her in an instant before she even hit the ground.

"You guys good?" she heard her father call in the dark.

"Yes... I tripped, but I'm fine," she replied, as Ash continued to hold her. His arms lingered on hers, reluctant to let go.

They both knew he could have let go and continued looking for his pack.

He *should* have let go, but here in the dark, no one could see them. The darkness was beginning to feel more like a warm embrace as she stood next to him. She made no moves to pull away from him either.

Her father was patiently waiting for Ash to light the lantern while Dax was busy recounting his brief interaction with the girl and wishing he could have stayed with her. She could sense her father's impatience with the boy even in the dark.

"Hey, could everyone help me feel around for the pack I left in here?" Ash asked gruffly, feigning an inability to find it. She hoped that only she had noticed the slight hoarseness to his voice.

As the others began to fumble around the black room searching for a pack, moving farther and farther away from them, he pulled Adelia closer. He wrapped his arms around her hips, holding her in the dark.

"*Ash,*" she whispered to him in a scolding tone, but even as she protested, her pulse sped up. He slid his fingers under the hem of her shirt, brushing against the sensitive skin there. It sent shivers down her spine as she imagined him tracing circles elsewhere.

She was thankful for the cover of darkness as her gaze dipped lower inadvertently, and a flush crept up her neck.

"I think I might have left the pack farther down the passage-way," Ash announced to the room.

"Fine, we'll look farther down," Dax grumbled, and with her father they shuffled farther down the path in the dark, away from them. Their footsteps rounded the corner, leaving Ash and Adelia alone in the dark.

The cloak of darkness hid them, and the others were distracted. Being this close to him was intoxicating. They weren't in the Molten castle; they were in their own cocoon of desire that was building with each moment they stood together. All she felt was his breath on her lips and the heat from his body pulsing out in waves. A rumble of lava from down the dark path filled the area with noise, hiding their whispers.

He moved then, unable to resist the urge any longer, pushed her into the wall.

Her back collided with the stone and Ash pressed his hips into hers. "I have wanted to do this for so damn long, Adelia."

He ground against her and she let out a small, breathy gasp. Sliding a leg between hers, he pinned her in place.

He grabbed her wrists and lifted them up above her head, flush to the wall. In this position, her chest was pressed up against him, and the material covering her breasts felt too thick. He bent his head down to her exposed neck and she found herself utterly at his command. And she was *very* okay with it.

"Do you have any idea what you do to me, Adelia?" he whispered.

He brushed featherlight kisses along her neck to her collarbone and it took every ounce not to moan for more.

"Ash," she whimpered, straining to keep her voice from sounding too desperate. He hadn't even kissed her and she was burning up with desire.

"*Shh.*" He bent down and whispered into her ear, his hot breath caressing her neck. "Tell me no and I'll stop."

"No—" she began. And Ash froze. She swore he stopped breathing.

"No, don't stop. I mean," she whispered, chuckling. He deserved a little bit of teasing after everything.

His face was close to hers now, and she felt a ghost of a smirk on his lips. He let go of one hand to gently pull on a curl playfully.

"Being this close to you, Adelia, I just... you're just..."

She wished she could see his face, to see his warm caramel eyes and infuriating smirk, to see if his eyes reflected the need that was evident in his voice and his touch.

His desire for her was palpable in the air, matching the passion coursing through her. Their closeness in the darkness felt forbidden, and that was exhilarating. She could feel his well-defined chest and powerful legs. And something else, pressed up against her that brought a blush to her cheeks.

She *needed* to be closer, to feel more of him.

The darkness was calling out to her, urging her to do more. Her body responded by arching up against him. She ground her hips against his, and he struggled to stifle a moan of his own.

"*Shhh,*" she whispered back playfully, and he let out a low, throaty growl that was drowned out in the rumbling of the river.

Hearing him unravel at her touch, she imagined, was like forbidden magic. She wanted to see what she could do to make him moan again, to see what reactions touching him in other places would elicit. She relished this feeling, never wanted it to end, and would do anything to keep it going. The darkness beckoned them to continue, for *more*.

She lifted her hand up as she had done in the dungeons, and this time she fed it into his tousled grey hair. She pulled him down towards her. He complied, his soft lips skating across her as he gripped her tighter.

"Adelia," he whispered in worship, then kissed her.

His mouth claimed hers, parting her lips slightly, and pressed into her further. She felt weak, but he supported her in his strong arms. His hips pressed up against hers harder in desperation, and he deepened the kiss further.

His body was hard and muscled against hers, her Molten Prince.

Because he was hers, and she was his.

There really never was any denying it.

Time stood still as their mouths moved against one another as if no one else existed in the world. She pulled her other hand away from the wall and threaded her fingers through his hair, pulling him deeper into the kiss. He nipped at her lip playfully, tugging it between his teeth. She could feel him against her, meeting all her soft spots with his hard ones. One of his hands cupped her face, and the other itched to discover more of her.

She had never felt anything like this before.

His tongue brushed her lips and she opened her mouth more to let him in. The sweeping of his tongue in her mouth set her skin on fire.

His hands drifted down to her waist again and around her backside to cup the soft curves of her ass. Then without warning, he lifted her up, her back still pressed up against the wall.

Adelia wrapped herself around him as best as she could.

She could feel all of him now. His generous length that she knew would be blissfully earth-shattering.

She wanted him. She wanted all of him.

It was just him and her in their cocoon of darkness.

The kiss was fireworks on a dark night, blazing up to light the velvet sky.

It was raging heat and crackling fire. Adelia knew she would be okay to stay here in his arms forever.

She moved her hands to lift up his shirt, to explore more of him, but he stopped her. His hands came to rest on her forearms as he pulled away from the kiss, leaving her lips cold and wanting in his absence.

"As much as I want that, we probably shouldn't do that here," he whispered, his grin audible. "I don't want you to have to hold back those moans next time, Goldilocks."

Just then, Dax called, "Found it!"

Ash placed her gently back on the ground and stepped away from her, leaving her breathless and frazzled. It had probably only been seconds that she and Ash stood there together, but it had felt like a lifetime.

"Great, now let's get some light in this hellhole," Ash replied, no hint of what had transpired traceable in his voice.

As Dax found the matches, lit the lantern, and cast the room in dim golden light, Adelia was grateful. Grateful that the light was so weak no one would be able to see the colour still burning in her cheeks or how her hair was slightly more tangled than before.

THE TUNNEL WAS DANK, dark, and smelled like smoke. They walked along a thin, precarious pathway adjacent to a thin stream of thick flowing lava. It had a slight current that sloshed along, bubbling up every few minutes to break the tense silence. They followed the river farther and farther away from the heart of the castle and every step they took made Adelia feel lighter.

It was the complete opposite feeling she had when they arrived here. She was leaving with her dad, who she had worried was already dead.

But here he was, and they were almost out.

She kept glancing back at the tunnel the way they came, fully expecting Molten soldiers to come barreling down the sewer to stop them.

But they never came.

She still couldn't believe what she and Ash had done back there. What had come over her? It was like reasonable Adelia, who knew they were trying to escape for their lives, had just left the building. She didn't regret it, though. Not one bit. She'd never been kissed like that in her life.

Eventually, they reached a grate blocking any further progress from the city. It was made of thick metal bars criss-crossing above the molten river and their current pathway.

But on the other side?

She could see the stars twinkling through gaps in the smoke and fog.

It was the city. They had made it out of the castle safely. The tunnel looked like it opened up into a back alley away from the main village. Once the grate was opened, they were free.

She had been trapped below ground for so long, she had forgotten what fresh air tasted like. Every breath beneath the volcano had stung her throat and constricted her airways.

She was fairly certain as a Wind Fae she was not meant to be trapped underground without access to fresh air.

Adelia closed her eyes and savored the moment, basking in the dense relief she felt.

Beside her, Ash grabbed hold of the bars and pulled his face closer to the grate to look at their surroundings and determine where they were.

"I think we're actually fairly close to the river. It's hard to see from here, but it looks pretty deserted out there."

Then a face peered around the corner of the grate.

A face that was charred and melting, with a grin as feral as the darkest creatures that dwelled in the Blacklore Woods.

"Hello, dear Prince," he seethed and reached an enormous hand through the bars of the grate with unparalleled speed. He wrapped an iron grip around Ash's throat and squeezed.

CHAPTER 40

The abrupt stop to the flow of air had Ash reeling. Adelia could see the shock in his eyes from the sudden appearance of the Molten Fae, as they all were.

Clearly fighting to ignore the urge to claw at his throat, he unsheathed his sword in one quick motion. He had always been a quick thinker and even quicker to act. He swung the glowing sword above his head in a sweeping arc and down onto the Molten's arms without missing a beat. The blade sliced clean through the Fae's wrists, severing through muscle and bone. The Fae's piercing screams echoed through the sleeping town, shattering the silence.

His dismembered hands fell from Ash's throat and hit the ground with a sickening thud.

He sucked in a breath and stumbled backwards.

They wouldn't be able to get out this way. They were trapped.

Adelia turned to start sprinting back down the tunnel, but her father grabbed her hand.

He shook his head. "If we go back that way and are cornered, it's all over. At least out here in the open we stand a chance. It's now or never, Adelia."

Ash nodded in agreement as he stood on alert in front of the gate. No other guards had dared to attack yet, but no doubt more lay in wait. "He's right, Adelia. We'd be playing right into her hands if we went back. And I wouldn't be able to pretend anymore to be a good little Prince. She'll know I tried to escape and freed you all."

"I'm scared," she whispered hoarsely.

Her dad pulled her into one last quick hug. "I know. But being scared is what makes us different from them. Because we have something to fight for. Something to lose. So be scared. Be scared, but stand tall and face your fear head-on."

And he was right.

If they returned into the volcano, they would be walking right back into the arms of their enemy. At least out here they could taste freedom on the wind. That, and three of them were Wind Fae. In the volcano, their powers were dampened. At least out here they could use the elements to their advantage.

She nodded back to him and squeezed his hand in solidarity.

This was only the beginning of her adventure.

Her drab, monotonous world had transformed into one of colour and magic, and she was finally starting to find her place in this world.

She looked at Ash, and then at her father.

She was here because of both of them.

She would live. She wouldn't let her fear dictate her actions but propel her forward.

Ash had his swords, her dad had his powers back, Dax had his cunning charm, and she had the will-power of iron.

Three Wind Fae and the best swordsman she had ever seen.

They could do this.

Before she had time to second-guess, the grate came crashing down. The entire thing had been ripped from its rusty hinges, courtesy of the Molten outside, and it fell to the ground with a resounding *bang*. Dax was the first to rush out, no fear in his wild eyes.

He threw his arms out and a tornado of wind exploded out, throwing all the Molten closest to them away. His hair blew wildly around his face and Adelia finally understood how he had been a guard. His easy smile was gone, replaced with an absolutely fearsome look. It had been easy to underestimate him. His explosion of wind strong enough to flay skin gave the rest of them a chance to step out from the grate into a small dip in the road.

They were surrounded by an army of Molten.

It was evident their plan to sneak out of the castle was never going to work. The Queen was no fool. She knew Ash's loyalties had lain elsewhere the whole time.

Adelia looked at the decaying Molten Fae around them, with lava seeping from every orifice. Their eyes were empty of all emotion other than burning anger. These Fae had succumbed to forbidden magic so fiercely, Adelia had to wonder if they would even feel any pain if they died.

She looked over at Ash in panic, hoping he had some brilliant plan to get them away from the throngs of Molten converging on them.

But all she saw was a sad determination in his eyes.

Like he was giving up.

But that wasn't the Ash she had grown to know.

It didn't make sense.

"Stay back, Adelia," he told her and stepped forwards.

It happened before she had time to comprehend his words. One moment, he was standing there, his grey hair almost silver in the moonlight, and then everything was red.

311

His blackened hands were consumed with fire and he was burning like a god. The flames grew wildly around him, framing his head in a glowing halo of fire.

Adelia stood frozen in utter shock. These weren't the meager flames of the Molten guards. This was the power of a Molten Prince.

He was born of smoke and fire, and it lived in his veins. His power was greater than anything she had ever seen before. His flames grew further until they stretched out on either side of him like two great burning wings. He looked like a fallen angel.

The Molten around them were too senseless to register the danger he posed.

They came at him with their fire and fury, trying to match him, but his flames licked out like whips at each one that dared to step close enough.

Each one disintegrated in seconds.

They fell like leaves after the first frost, dead before they could even hit the floor.

All evidence of their existence was swept away with the wind.

Ash held the power of the volcano itself in his hands. The meaning of his name all the more clear with each fallen Fae.

His raging fire consumed the street, rolling off of him in waves. The light grew so bright that Adelia had to shield her eyes from the glow.

Then he slowly started moving forwards. He forged a path for them with flames and she fueled his fire with wind to help it grow. There is no fire without air. The guards had continually repeated that they were stronger together, and this was proof.

Adelia's power stoked his flames and her pain fueled his anger. His anger only gave her faith that they were unstoppable.

Ash moved through the city in a trance, wiping from existence every Molten who got close. When they reached the lava river, Adelia had no idea how they would cross. Without Rory's powers to build them a raft, they would be trapped again. She looked over her shoulder at the Molten that were desperately attempting to get past Ash's fire. They were relentless, sacrificing themselves to the flames to try and breach his defenses.

But then Ash lifted his blazing hands and held them out to the raging river below them. The lava sloshing past paused in its path and began to rise like it was weightless. The lava rose till it was level with the ground and then froze mid-air. With a flourish of his flaming hands, the lava solidified and before them was a perfectly smooth basalt bridge. Steam wafted from the bridge into the air around as it cooled.

Without a glance back, Ash strode across the bridge, and the rest of them followed.

When they reached the other side, Adelia looked over her shoulder to see what was left of the Molten army staring at them from across the river. She was unsure whether they had orders to fall back or if they had realized they were no match for Ash. Regardless, they didn't follow.

Ash raised his arms again, his caramel eyes alight with fire, and called the lava from the river once again. It rose to the level of the bridge and consumed it once more. But instead of just destroying the bridge, the lava spilled from the riverbanks and into the slumbering city. With eerie sentience, the lava crept silently along the cobblestone roads, closer and closer to the quiet homes filled with sleeping Molten Fae.

It flooded the streets, melting the roads, and then reached the homes. Adelia watched as the ones not made of stone erupted into flames. The flames licked along the baseboards and up the walls to the thatched roofs of home after home. The cloying scent of smoke thickened around them until everyone but Ash was coughing wildly.

Adelia looked over at him in alarm, only to realize in horror how far gone he was.

She had been so caught up in their brilliant escape that she hadn't taken the time to actually look at him.

His features seemed inhuman, and his eyes cold and dark.

All his warmth was gone, replaced by bloodlust.

If he didn't stop, he'd kill every last Molten in the city.

Women.

Children.

All the innocents who had already been trapped here for decades.

But how was she supposed to stop him when his skin was on fire?

"Ash! Ash, stop!" she yelled at him. "We did it! We escaped! You can stop now!" It was useless. He was completely overtaken by his power.

Her father and Dax joined in, trying to snap him out of his trance. Dax picked up stones and tried chucking them at Ash's face, but they made no impact.

"What the fuck, Ash! Wake up! Don't do this!" Dax screamed at him.

But the lava kept flowing.

She watched in horror as across the river, Fae were climbing onto the roofs of their homes to escape the lava bubbling up below them. One mother shoved her young daughter up onto the roof as the lava rose to her ankles and she screamed in pain. She could see the daughter trying to reach down to pull her mom up onto the roof with frantic sobs. They were both still in their pajamas.

Ash had once told her that the stronger the Fae, the greater their resistance to disaster. A royal Snow Fae could withstand ice and cold without ever even feeling the effects of frostbite, but a lesser Fae? They could most certainly succumb to the elements despite their powers. It was similar with Molten Fae. Any of the innocents who lived in the village could surely harness the power of lava, but that didn't make their skin completely fire-proof. And if they didn't stop Ash soon, they would all be swimming in lava.

Adelia moved to stand in front of Ash to block his view of the carnage, but it didn't matter. He looked right through her as though she were invisible.

She could only think of one other thing to try. It was stupid. But it was the only idea she had.

She reached out and grabbed his face between her hands, wincing at the flames that licked her palms. They instantly burned, blistering at the touch, but she held fast.

"Ash, listen to me!" She tried to imbue her voice with power, to sound more confident than she felt.

God, it burned.

It burned so much.

She could barely focus. "Ash, you are not a monster. Your powers, your flames, they don't make you evil. They never have. You don't have to do this. You don't want to kill innocent Fae. I know you don't."

She willed him to see the faith she had in him. She tried to show it with her eyes and have it seep through her touch.

"I know you're in there," she whispered.

Then, finally, he looked at her. He dragged his eyes away from the destruction he was raining down upon the city and looked at her with cold, unseeing eyes that rivaled Maewyn's ice daggers.

As if in slow motion, he reached his hands up and placed his palms on her hands still holding his face. Then he pressed them harder into his burning skin with a dark chuckle, as if her pain amused him.

"Ash! What are you doing? This hurts!"

But he didn't budge, and her hands burned more.

The pain was blinding, her vision blurred at the edges.

She tried desperately to rip her hands away from his face, screaming, "Let me go, Ash!"

And that's when she felt it.

A faint tug deep inside her core, growing with intensity.

Ash's sadistic grin was so much like his mother's as he began to drain the power from Adelia's soul.

Teilio and Dax could feel the shift in the air, and they rushed to her aid. Dax jumped into the air for Ash's back, as nimble as a falcon diving, while her dad went to attempt to wrench his hands away.

Ash responded with an explosion of fire that sent them careening backwards.

Adelia watched in horror as her dad crumpled to the ground ten feet away, smoldering from the explosion. Dax flew in the other direction, hitting the ground with a sickening thud.

The intensity of his pull increased, and she screamed out in pain.

"Please. Please fight this," she sobbed, still trying desperately to wrench his hands away from hers.

Ash's eyes were alight with flames, as he dug his claws into her soul and tried to rip it from her. He had no control over what he was doing, and she was powerless.

So Adelia stopped trying to fight him and let her body relax. Instead, she leaned in and pressed her lips softly to his in a last-ditch effort before her knees gave way.

Please, Ash. Come back to me.

And then she saw the shift in his eyes from her featherlight kiss.

His unseeing eyes, consumed by his power, slowly focused on hers as he was returning back to himself.

His hands fell limply at his sides and Adelia sagged in relief.

The power he had been siphoning returned to her body. Then the lava began to recede. It moved away from the homes and sank back down into the river. She could hear the sobs of relief of the Molten Fae from across moat.

Ash wavered on his feet, then fell to his knees, skidding into the dirt. Adelia kneeled down to join him and wrapped her arms around him. She held him in her arms and smoothed his sooty hair back from his forehead. He was coated in a sheen of sweat and still burning up from the fire that had been licking at his skin seconds before.

"Shhh, it's okay. You're okay."

But he wasn't okay.

The look in his eyes was gut-wrenching.

He stared in horror across the river at the smoldering homes and bodies in the streets.

At the deaths he had caused. He couldn't even bring himself to look at her. She could feel his hesitation at her closeness by the tension in his body. Like he was afraid to give in and embrace her after what he had just done.

She saw regret, guilt, and utter self-loathing in his caramel eyes and she wished she could take it all from him.

Because she knew he had done it to save them. He had reached down to that power he kept hidden away for so long to get them out.

He was willing to risk himself and his sanity to save her. It was clear he didn't know how dangerous he could be, though. And she would never condemn him for that despite how close he had been to the edge, or for the lives he took today.

She knew him.

She knew he wasn't evil. He didn't live his life with hatred and violence like his mother.

Ash had made a choice.

A choice Adelia would be forever grateful for.

His choice to use his powers he could barely control was going to give her a second chance at life. She would have more moments to spend with her father and more time to explore their blossoming relationship.

He had given her a lifetime of possibilities.

He'd have to figure out how to atone for the deaths he caused later. How to live with the choice he had made.

Adelia stroked his hair over and over again monotonously, holding him tight in her arms. She cradled him as if he were a child, afraid he would break if she let go. Her dad and Dax recovered and moved to stand nearby, unsure of what to do.

Adelia tried to hold him tight enough to keep him from falling apart, from falling into that abyss.

But his eyes were empty again.

Not with a violent lust but horror at what unfolded at his hands.

His eyes were locked on the city before them like he was unable to fully comprehend what he had done.

She wasn't sure how he did it either.

His power was terrifying and monstrous, but she wasn't afraid. Even as she held him, knowing he was most likely the most dangerous Fae in this world, she wasn't afraid.

She scooted around on her knees so that she was facing him. She reached her now wounded hands back up to his face and pulled him towards her.

"Ash. I know telling you that you had to or that you couldn't control it won't make it better. It won't change anything. But what I do know is that I'm not afraid. I'm not afraid of you or your power. I see you. I can see your heart, full of compassion and resilience. I see your fears, guilt, and regret and they make you human. I see your courage, dedication, and desire to help others. I see the love you hold in your heart for everyone but yourself. You are *good*, Ash. And nothing you did today changes that."

She wanted to tell him so badly.

She wanted to tell him how she felt, what had been growing in her heart since the moment she met him. The feeling she had that being with him was just *right*.

But he was so broken at that moment.

And she knew it wasn't the right time.

He looked up at her, devastation written across his features.

"I killed them all," he whispered, his voice breaking in agony. "I almost killed *you*."

She saw tears welling, threatening to spill over, and it only broke her heart more.

Her cocky, arrogant Prince.

Everything he did was for other people. He couldn't let his guilt consume him like this. It broke her to see him with such hatred in his eyes. Hatred for himself and the powers he thought were a curse.

Adelia nodded.

There was no denying what he had done.

"Yes," she whispered. "But giving up now means it was all for nothing. Closing yourself off and never using your powers again doesn't save all these Fae. Or me. I need you, Ash. I need you to get out of here safely. And then we work together to stop your mom. I am right here, and I'm not ever leaving. And I'll be right beside you as you learn to properly control your powers. And then we will come back here to stop her. Because that's really what these people deserve. A chance to be free of her. And only you can do that. Don't close up on me now."

She didn't know if he would ever trust himself again, whether he could move on from this. But they didn't have time to sit and contemplate life. He had saved them, and she knew they had to make it mean something.

They had to move.

She rose, gingerly pulling him to his feet with her, and he followed.

She nodded to her dad and Dax and, with one last look, left the smoldering city behind to become nothing but smoke and ash.

CHAPTER 41

The four of them trudged away from the Molten Court in silence.

Adelia kept her hand firmly in Ash's, determined to keep him tethered to this world in both body and mind.

None of them spoke of what had happened. Maybe they would one day, but for now, they had to move forward. At least until they knew they were safe, and she didn't have to keep looking over her shoulder to see if the Molten had followed them.

Adelia gazed at the stars above them, her heart beating in a steady rhythm that seemed to pulse in time with the twinkling. She prayed for the cover of darkness for a bit longer to give them a chance to escape.

Finally, they caught three figures making their way towards them, and she almost burst into tears. Maewyn's white hair flowed behind her, looking like a glistening river of light in the cover of darkness. Beside her walked Rory and Novak, and finally, little Rin trotting behind them.

They were alive.

They had *all* made it out alive.

It seemed like a miracle.

"We were coming to look for you!" Maewyn started but then caught the look on Ash's face. "Wait, what happened?"

Adelia shook her head and mouthed the words *not now*.

Maewyn seemed to understand.

"Come on, we found a small grove back there that's pretty hidden. We can rest up there for a bit. Will they come searching for you?" Novak asked.

Teilio answered, "Yes."

Nothing else needed to be said. They probably had very little time to bandage their wounds and drink some water before someone tried to follow.

Novak cornered Adelia on the walk back, leaving enough space between them so that Ash couldn't overhear.

"What happened in there, Adelia?" She glanced surreptitiously at Ash's hands behind them, and Adelia followed her gaze with a sigh.

"I think that's Ash's story to tell. When he's ready."

Novak nodded. "Fair enough. I shouldn't be surprised. He was never particularly good at lying. We all knew there was more to him than he let on. I just didn't expect him to be Molten..."

Ha. Not just any Molten, Adelia thought. "Are you mad he lied to you?" she asked Novak carefully.

Novak sighed and kicked at the stone in their way. "I should be. I should be angry he lied to us about being Molten. But it wouldn't have changed anything. He's family. He never put us in danger with his lie, and he never betrayed us. I assume he thought we'd never find out, so it would never matter."

Then Adelia filled her in on what had happened with his powers. Novak listened intently as her face grew more and more solemn.

"He's never going to forgive himself." She shook her head, letting her blue bangs fall over her eyes. "It was incredibly stupid. But brave. I really wouldn't have expected anything less. On another note, what the hell is Dax doing with you?"

"Oh. Yeah, we found him in the dungeon."

Novak laughed. "That idiot. I'm not surprised in the slightest. He better not expect me to welcome him back with open arms." Her eyes narrowed. "You don't abandon your team and then waltz back expecting all to be forgiven."

"He doesn't seem *that* bad." She looked back to see Dax chatting playfully with Maewyn. Maewyn was visibly enjoying his company and kept swinging her hands wildly around as she filled him in on the past year's events. She kept stealing sheepish glances back at Novak like she'd get in trouble for not being mad at him too.

"Oh, just wait. He's self-entitled and arrogant. He'll show his true colours soon enough."

"Okay, my turn. What happened to Maewyn? Why are her eyes glowing red...?"

"We aren't entirely sure what the implications will be... but it seems Maewyn has both fire and ice powers now."

"Excuse me?" Adelia sputtered.

Novak sighed. "I've been trying to give Maewyn some space to deal with it. I think she's pretty torn up. We'll have to fill you both in on everything that happened after we regroup."

They arrived at the small grove and sat down. Rory began bandaging Adelia's hands. Her dad nestled in beside her while Ash took the left. He was still hollow and disengaged.

It gave her a moment to think about what happened and what she should do now. She was tired of lying. Tired of this whole mess she had gotten them into.

She knew what needed to be done.

"Uhh... guys. I need to tell you all something."

She subconsciously lifted her hand to her throat to touch the tiny key that had made its home there. Its subtle heat had become a comfort. A reminder of what she was fighting for —her dad.

But he was here now, and using this key was maybe their only chance at locking the Molten up again. They all knew the Queen was planning to attack the Wind Court. She didn't know when exactly, but she wasn't willing to take a risk.

She lifted her hands up and slowly removed the key from her neck. She held it out in her palm to show them all.

Ash, still quieter than usual, was the first to speak.

"You found the key in the castle? Where? How?" he croaked.

She shook her head.

"No... I didn't find it in the castle."

They all looked at her, confused, including her dad, who wasn't aware she had withheld this information from them. She never told him she planned for him to say he had it the whole time. That lie would have never worked anyway. He had been in the Molten Court for so long, the Queen would have found it.

And she was done with lies.

They had become friends. They deserved to know the truth.

"I've had the key the whole time," she whispered.

She thought once she said the words, she wouldn't feel as guilty.

But it was almost worse.

Their looks of confusion, their realization that she had lied on their stricken faces, was horrible.

The confession made her lie real. The lie had been swirling around her, a dark companion on her journey. Always hovering around her, but never corporeal.

Now it was tangible. It had materialized in front of her, forcing her to confront the consequences.

"I never meant for it to be like this... I just... I just wanted to save my dad, and I was worried you would all take the key from me and leave. I knew I couldn't do it alone."

It was Maewyn who spoke first. "Does that mean you were only using us?"

"No!" Adelia quickly interrupted. "Well, maybe at first, but that was before I knew you all. I never wanted to hurt anyone... but I didn't stand a chance at saving him without you."

"You didn't think you could trust us?" The fact that it was Maewyn asking this made it all the worse. She wanted them to be angry, but this was so much worse.

They were hurt.

She could see it in their eyes.

They had trusted her, had accepted her as part of their team, but she had been lying to them this whole time.

She didn't have an excuse.

She *should* have trusted them.

She had wanted to so badly, but her own insecurities had prevailed. Even after everything that had been growing between her and Ash, she still hadn't told him.

What did that say about her?

She wanted Ash to say something, *anything*.

But he stayed silent.

He refused to look at her like he had done in the castle when she found out he was a Molten Prince. He had lied and betrayed her then, and now she had done the same thing.

"I'm sorry. I'm so sorry." She wouldn't cry. Not now. "I trust you all with my life. I don't know why I didn't tell you. I was so worried you would leave!"

"But we're friends, Adelia!" Maewyn snapped. She had never seen the girl even moderately angry before. Her new fiery eyes flashed. "And friends don't lie."

"How is this any different than Ash lying about being

Molten?" she retorted, and Ash flinched at her harsh words. She should feel guilty, but this felt hypocritical.

Novak snapped back, "Because Ash lying about being Molten never put us at risk. You realize you just took a dangerous magical object into the *one* place you shouldn't have brought it and only managed to get out by the skin of your teeth? What would have happened if Queen Karai had found out you had it? Were you prepared to condemn all of Faerie? It could have been so simple, Adelia. You could have told us and we could have found a safe place for the key before planning a rescue mission for your dad. We were never the bad guys. We're the Faerie Guard! Our job is to protect people!"

"You're really telling me you wouldn't have used the key and trapped my dad there?"

Maewyn looked at her with teary eyes. "I would have helped you, Adelia."

Rory finally spoke, "I don't blame you for thinking that when you first met us. But now? You should have known we wouldn't have left you, Adelia. I didn't think you thought so little of us."

"No, that's not it—" she started, but Novak interrupted.

"I think we need to go talk alone for a few minutes," Novak announced. She looked at Adelia as she finished. "As a *team*." She emphasized the word team, and it was crystal clear that it did not include her.

She was not a part of their team.

She had ruined that.

She was just a Fae girl from the human world. No real home, no real friends.

But then her dad slipped an arm around her shoulders.

He pulled her into a hug, one of those hugs that could hold all your pieces together when you were falling apart.

"They'll come around, Addy. I will forever be in your debt

for what you did. You are so brave, and you had to make hard choices. They'll forgive you eventually. They just need some space."

Ash, Novak, Maewyn, Rory, and even Dax made to leave their little grove and descend farther into the Blacklore Woods.

Rory purposely walked close to Adelia and her dad before he followed.

"For what it's worth, Adelia, I get it. I get why." And then he followed them into the woods.

CHAPTER 42

S he sat in silence with her dad around the small campfire. He had tried to console her, but it hadn't really worked. Instead, she stared at the flames. Their heat warmed the cool air blowing in from the woods behind them. Adelia held her hands toward it and watched them glow golden. The smoke twirled heavenward, and she tried to relax into the sound of the wood crackling.

They had been gone for so long, she had begun to wonder if they had left. Maybe they had gone into the woods, decided she wasn't worth it, and kept walking.

She wouldn't blame them, not really. Even though it would break her heart.

She was still angry, but she also understood how careless she had been in bringing the key with them.

Before long, the sun was starting to rise, bringing copper hues and a gentle warm embrace of rays. Adelia watched as her dad was cast in crimson and gold while she sat as a silhouette, the sun not quite reaching her. It seemed like the sun was honouring him and his goodness. He was worthy of the sun's embrace, and she sat undeserving in the shadows.

Finally, she heard rustling in the bushes and the sound of approaching feet.

Relief flooded through her. They had come back.

They hadn't left her!

She jumped up, along with her dad, to greet them as they pushed through the throngs of brush, but instead, she saw a stranger's face.

The face of a Molten Guard.

Oh, God, they came, Adelia thought.

"They're over here!" he called. He was still relatively far away, but in no time, he would be on them.

Adelia turned around to see a dozen Molten Fae converging on them, more than they could fight alone.

She needed the others.

Her team.

Because they *were* a team, despite what Novak had said when they left.

She may have lied about having the key, and they might be hurt, but she knew now they were better together. She thought back to the oath Maewyn told her they had all taken before joining the guard.

May we always bear faith and allegiance to our fellow guard, for their strength is our strength, their power our power. Only together are we whole.

Together they were whole.

Alone they were half as strong as they could be when they worked together. Each time they faced trouble, they all contributed in their own way to push the team towards success.

At the house fighting the Molten for the first time, in the Blacklore Woods, crossing the lava river, escaping from the

Molten castle. All of those things would have been impossible on her own.

She was about to call out for them—they couldn't have gone that far into the forest—when she heard a choked gurgle from behind her.

As if in slow motion, she spun around to see an arrow protruding from her dad's chest. Its thick wooden shaft lodged into his rib cage, with beautiful red and orange fletchings still vibrating from the impact.

He looked down in shock and reached his already blanched hand to the arrow in disbelief as if to feel if it was real.

He looked at Adelia, his eyes filled with panic, and he collapsed to his knees on the ground.

She rushed over to him and caught his head before it hit the ground.

She eased him down, frantically trying to process how to fix this.

How to reverse time.

The Molten were growing closer, and she threw out a wall of wind to throw the closest ones back. The force of the wind hit them, and a few Fae went flying through the air. She kept the wall of wind strong enough to keep them back from where she sat cradling her father.

The blood from his wound began to leak out, soaking his tattered shirt in red. It was as bright as a cardinal on a winter's day, but for Adelia, the moment felt grey.

Time itself became irrelevant. The seconds could have been hours, or hours mere seconds. She was frozen in a suspended moment inside the eye of a storm.

No horror she had ever experienced had prepared her for this. Not even seeing blood on her kitchen floor and knowing it was from him. It was nothing like this.

Tears streaming down her face, she watched as the life began to slowly ebb away from her father's eyes.

"No… no, no, no!" she screamed. "Dad! You're okay!"

She tried to put her hand around the arrow to staunch the bleeding. She knew she shouldn't yank the arrow out or he could bleed out faster. Even though every fibre of her being called for her to pull it out.

His bright hazel eyes fluttered as he looked at her. The endless love he felt for her was written across his face.

"I love you, sunshine," he murmured with visible effort.

He tried to reach up and touch her face, but his strength had left him. His arms lay limp at his side, unable to carry out the command.

"No, you can't leave me, Dad! Not now!" She was sobbing now, her tears a river.

But no matter how hard she pressed on the wound, the blood didn't relent. It oozed out from between her blood-stained fingers in time with his slowing pulse.

He was cold.

Too cold already.

"Ash! Novak! Rory! *Anyone!*" she sobbed.

They *had* to come back.

She needed them.

The Molten were getting closer again. Time only seemed to be standing still for her.

Adelia sobbed harder as her father's chest stuttered. His breathing became difficult and she could hear gurgling.

"Daddy, no. Help us!" She wailed into the wind. Praying that someone would come save him. Come save her.

She pushed her hands into his chest harder, hoping it would stop. But she felt the exact moment he stopped breathing. One second his chest was rising and falling, and next it wasn't.

This wasn't happening. It couldn't be happening.

Then she felt a searing pain in her back and whirled around to see a Molten flinging balls of fire at her.

She didn't have a chance of surviving if she couldn't stop these Molten. They would both die.

She didn't need her dad here to tell her that she needed to stop them, to leave him and protect herself. He'd never want her to give up. If he died now, knowing that she had rolled over and accepted death with him, he would be livid.

Tears still streaming down her face, she let go of the wound gingerly with a sob and stood.

She turned to face the monstrous soldiers making their way toward her again. Their hands were burned and oozing, and unrelenting rage glinted in their eyes. They were not in control of their own lust for violence, and she wasn't going to hold back either.

These Fae were fathers, mothers, brothers, and sisters.

But they had let the Queen convince them forbidden magic was their salvation.

Adelia mourned for the Fae they used to be as she reached out to the magic around her. She felt the tendrils around her and grasped at them desperately.

First, she felt the air, the wind, the breeze around her, but she needed more. She wouldn't die here today. Her dad would want her to live. To give everything she had to fight another day. And she'd do that for him.

She had to use every last ounce of power she was capable of.

She felt the familiar thrum of electricity in her veins, the spark of magic coming to life, and she reached up to the sky.

The wind picked up around them, swirling around and around. Leaves, branches, and pebbles were swept up from the forest floor in a tornado around her.

The wind whipped her hair erratically around her face, and the hair on her arms stood up.

But she needed *more*.

She pushed out again, feeling for more magic around her, and the sky answered her call.

She pulled the clouds in around her and saw them darkening the sky. They grew blacker until night had fallen over the grove again.

The sun was completely obscured.

She felt the magic in the clouds miles above her. She had never reached that far for her magic before, but she knew she could do it. She called the magic of the storm clouds down to her.

She opened her eyes in cold fury and directed the magic onto the converging horde of Molten soldiers around her.

Except this time, it wasn't just wind and air.

Lightning exploded from the stygian sky, forking down in a zigzag pattern.

It crackled and hissed with fury, angry as a vengeful god.

One bolt hit the Molten next to her, and he screamed.

He fell to the ground, dead.

There was no mercy in the violent voltage that exploded each time a bolt struck a Molten Fae. Electricity crackled in her veins, lighting her up from the inside out. Every hair stood on end as she called down more lightning.

More Fae swelled in retaliation, but the lightning answered, bolt after bolt exploding from the treacherous storm clouds and incinerating the Molten converging on her.

Adelia screamed but was drowned out by the resounding booms of thunder that shook the air. The thunder was the voice of lightning, and it was her drumroll. It set the stage for her final display of power, to show the Molten they had messed with the wrong girl.

She wasn't sure what was happening or how, but she wasn't about to stop.

The lightning crackled around her, electrifying her soul.

She locked eyes with a soldier who hurled a fireball at her chest. Time slowed as she danced out of the way and the fireball fell the tree behind her with its impact. She responded with a shot of lightning to the chest.

The Molten fell in hoards until finally, the clearing quieted.

She looked around to see hundreds of Molten soldiers lying in circles around her, never within ten feet of her father.

She didn't even have time to register what she had done.

How many people she had killed.

She rushed back over to her father, frantically feeling for a pulse.

But it wasn't there.

His chest was silent and his skin was cold.

Tears flowed again. "Please don't leave me. I need you, Dad," she begged, even though she knew it was too late. "There's still so much I wanted to ask you about. So much I wanted to tell you about. How am I ever going to go on without you?" She could barely get the words out.

Adelia dropped her head onto him and wept. All of this for nothing. She had lost him despite everything she had done to save him. Her friends had left, and now he was gone and she had no one left in this world. It felt like her heart was collapsing in on itself, a chasm forming in her chest, and Adelia knew it would never go away.

The one person she loved more than life itself was gone and she would never be the same again.

Adelia wept over her father and refused to move even as she heard five familiar pairs of feet running towards her.

CHAPTER 43

ASH

Ash knew something was wrong as soon as the sky started to darken. Moments before, the sun had been kissing the horizon, and then a storm had rolled in and darkened the heavens. The clouds were pregnant with malice, and he could feel the energy in the air.

It wasn't natural. He knew that much and it seemed to wake him from the daze he'd been in.

"We need to go! Now!" he barked and didn't wait for the others to follow.

He ran off into the forest, back towards Adelia and Teilio in the grove.

If something happened to her... he shook off the thought.

He couldn't think like that.

It just made him run faster. He bounded over fallen logs and ducked under branches, his clothes snagging on sharp thorns. He heard the sleeve of his shirt rip but kept running.

Then he heard it.

Thunder boomed, threatening to burst his eardrums. Thunder was the sky's call, and then the earth answered. Purple and black streaks of lightning ripping through the clouds, shooting down to the grove where they had left Adelia and Teilio.

It was strange enough that he almost paused… almost.

Molten couldn't call lightning. That was the lost power of the Storm Fae. There was no way…

It took too long to get back to the clearing. He hadn't even realized how far they had wandered.

He finally burst through the brush to find Adelia on her knees, sobbing.

She was cradling Teilio's head, her hands pressed to his chest, where he saw a telltale Molten arrow protruding.

"Oh God, Adelia, what happened?" he screamed as he ran towards them.

It was everything he feared.

He had left her.

It was only for a short time, but he had left her all the same.

He wasn't there, and the Molten had come for them.

How could he have been so stupid?

He fell to his knees beside her heaving body and looked at the wound in her father's chest. It was deep, and dark crimson blood had soaked the ground around them.

He scrambled over to Adelia, all thoughts of his powers leaving him. He lifted her from her father and cradled her in his arms, which only made her sob harder.

"I'm sorry, Adelia. I'm so sorry."

Maewyn and the others caught up and Novak proceeded to check Teilio's pulse. She shook her head silently at them to convey it wasn't there.

"He's gone, Ash. He's gone," she whispered. She looked at him with her beautiful hazel eyes, but there was so much pain in her features.

Her face was streaked with tears, her hair a static mess.

He didn't know what to say. What did one say in this situation? He wasn't going to tell her everything would be fine because it wasn't.

Ash turned to Adelia and reached for her trembling hands.

"Are you hurt?" He'd start there. Deal with any physical injuries first.

But she was still shell-shocked and didn't answer.

He reached out and lightly pulled her chin so that she was looking at him.

"Are you hurt anywhere, Adelia?"

She shook her head, seemingly incapable of words.

He nodded and cradled her to his chest again. Her sobs slowed as the others sat around them in stunned silence. They had been gone for such a short period of time, but so much had happened. Dozens of Molten Fae lay strewn around them as unmoving as Teilio.

What in the world had she done to them? Where did that power come from?

Ash held her tightly as she cried for as long as he dared. He wanted nothing more than to continue to hold and comfort her, but more soldiers were bound to come. They needed to move.

Otherwise, they ran the risk of being attacked again.

CHAPTER 44

He was dead. Her father was dead.

Her emotions were in absolute turmoil. It felt as if she was in the ocean after jumping off her cliff and the undertow was pulling her out to sea. She was struggling to get to the surface for a breath, but the waves kept dragging her down. Her grief was pulling her under, threatening to swallow her whole.

She didn't know how to cope. She didn't know how she should act or what to say. Right now it didn't even feel real. It felt like she was having a night terror again, and soon she'd wake up and go downstairs to find her dad in the kitchen with a cup of coffee for her.

But she knew deep down that this was real. Her dad was gone and he'd never bring her a cup of coffee again. He'd never call her sunshine or take her to the Bark Beach circus to see the trapeze artists. She wanted nothing more than to wallow in her grief, but she knew they had to move. The longer they waited here, the longer the Molten had to regroup and come after them.

Ash had pulled her to a standing position, silent worry on his face.

"We have an idea, Adelia. A way to stop the Molten. I know this will be hard for you, but we need to do it now."

She nodded and followed him to where the others were gathered a few paces away.

Once they were all standing in a small circle, he announced, "Okay, Adelia, you weren't there for the conversation we had, but we're going to use the key."

She looked at him incredulously.

"It will kill us!"

He shook his head. "No, we are all going to give it a drop of our power. Using it alone almost killed your father." He winced at the words. "But there are six of us now. If we all use it together, we can properly seal the gate this time. We can't wait around for another solution. Queen Karai will not wait. I can't have more innocent lives on my hands."

The others seemed to have already agreed to this as they stood silently while Ash explained.

Was this what they had been discussing when they had left? Maybe it wasn't about whether to leave her after all.

"Don't get me wrong, this is going to be dangerous. But we're all together again." He reached out his hand to Adelia, and she grabbed hold of it firmly. He reached his other hand out, and Rory clasped it.

The six of them formed a tight circle.

The Prince, the birdwatcher, the leader, the muscle, the optimist, and the flirt.

Six Fae from completely different upbringings, different courts, different worlds even.

But together, they were one.

They were halves of a whole.

Having them here filled the chasm in her heart a bit. She had thought she'd lost them as well. But they had only left to discuss how to use the key. They hadn't left her.

Adelia removed the key from her neck and held it out to Ash.

"I don't know what to do."

He took it from her, and it was still weird to see him without his gloves on. She found herself glancing down at his charred hands again and again.

"I've imbued items with magic before. I'll start the process, and the key will begin to siphon power from me. If we are all touching, it should begin to take some from all of us."

He drew in a breath and looked through the edge of the woods where the tip of the volcano was visible.

Ash closed his eyes, and all around Adelia could feel the air begin to warm up.

His face contorted at first in concentration and then in pain.

Eventually, she started to feel what he was feeling.

It was as if someone was tugging at her soul from a tether. It was coming from the hand holding Ash's, and the insistent pull grew greater and greater.

It took every last bit of her willpower to keep holding on. Every fibre told her to let go, to not give up even an ounce of this newfound power.

But behind her eyes, the people, the world she was fighting for flashed before her.

Her father who was gone too early but would want her to live a long, happy life. The Fae of the Wind Court—the women and children who were just beginning to heal after the horrors of the last war. She saw the faces of her new friends and how she needed the chance to show them how much they meant to her. She saw Ash and the spark that had begun to blossom between them. She wanted the time to explore that more and see where it led. She cared for him more than she had cared for anyone other than her family, which was so new and unfamiliar.

So Adelia held on.

She held on as the key began to siphon her power from her veins. It started as a flutter of wind flowing down her arm to her fingertips where Ash clasped her hand, and her fingers shook with the strain.

She remembered the memory Tadriel had shown them and how using the key had almost killed her father then. But he persevered. And she would too. She steeled herself as he did and imagined he was here with her. She let the vacuum take the kernel of power she was offering up.

She strained to open her eyes and looked at the rest of the team. They all had their faces contorted in concentration as well. She knew they must all be feeling the same thing. They all were sacrificing a small kernel of their power to the key.

She began to feel a fullness as the seconds passed, like the key had almost had its fill. At that moment, a shimmering bubble extended from above the clouds.

She watched in awe as the dome descended around the Molten Court, eventually lowering past the tree line and out of sight.

The barrier was forming.

They were doing it.

Adelia's arms and legs were shaking as she tried to hold on for a few more seconds.

It felt too easy. She hadn't come close to dying. They had each only had to sacrifice a small amount of their power. The Molten would be locked away again.

Queen Karai wouldn't be able to hurt anyone else.

There wouldn't be another war.

They could escape today and she would *live*.

The vacuum seemed to lessen its hold on her slightly and the pulling lessened. It was almost full.

She looked around and knew everyone was feeling the same thing. Their faces were a mixture of relief and exhaustion.

She couldn't help the smile that blossomed on her face.

She looked up at Ash beside her to find him looking back down at her with a small smile and sad eyes.

Wait, why would he be sad at a moment like this? she thought.

And then she noticed.

The edges of his sculpted chest, his arms, and face were blurring around the edges slightly.

What in the world...

"Ash, what's going on...?" Her momentary relief was ebbing away as he slowly faded. His entire figure seemingly dispersing into the wind.

He was becoming transparent.

"Adelia, I want you to know how much I care about you. I want you to go live your life. With your new friends. You have a long, happy life ahead of you. I just want you to be happy. I wanted you to be safe." He looked around at Novak, Rory, Dax, and Maewyn. "They'll protect you. We all actually think you'd make a great Faerie Guard."

"What, no? Ash, what are you saying?"

Why, why is he saying these things?

He continued, "But I need you to promise me you won't come looking for me. You need to move on. This is for all of Faerie." He chuckled darkly to himself. "That makes me sound like a hero. Which I'm definitely not, but maybe this will start to make up for all the things my family and I have done. All the death and destruction."

He was fading more with each passing second, and Adelia knew as soon as the key was full of magic, he would be gone.

She remembered in horror that this was the original function of the key.

Its purpose was to stop a war and lock all the Molten Fae behind the gate forever.

When her dad first used the key, he had stopped before it was full of magic. It had only formed a semi-solid barrier. It had trapped the Molten already inside the court, but anyone outside hadn't been banished back to their homeland.

Ash hadn't been inside the court when her dad used the key.

He hadn't been trapped.

But now?

Now, they had managed to use their magic together to properly seal the gate. Which meant any Molten Fae outside its borders would be transported back and locked away with all the others.

Ash was going to be trapped inside the Molten Court, to endure its horrors and his psychopathic mother for the rest of his long life.

"No. No, no, NO!" Adelia screamed.

Tears welled up in her eyes again.

"You can't leave me, Ash, not now. I need you."

"No, you don't, Adelia. You've never needed anyone." There was awe in his eyes again.

She tried to pull her hand free of his, but he wouldn't let go.

He was just a faint silhouette now. Like he was a ghost passing through their world.

Maybe that's what he had always been.

Living on borrowed time, waiting for the moment when the Molten Fae he detested claimed him again.

She continued to try and pry her hands from both his and Novak's on her other side, but they both held her tight.

She looked over at Novak in betrayal, but she shook her head.

"You knew! You knew and were okay with this?" she screamed at her, trying to thrash away from them both. "How dare you! What happened to being a team! To nobody gets left behind!"

"Adelia," Ash said to her softly. Even his voice sounded distant now.

"I wish we had more time too." She watched him smile sadly again. "I always knew I'd fall in love with you."

And then he disappeared into the wind, and her hand fell limply to her side.

She ripped her hand from Novak's to grasp at the air, trying to catch him before he disappeared.

But there was nothing but air.

Ash was gone.

CHAPTER 45

Adelia knew she was walking and breathing but couldn't bring herself to think or speak.

She was numb.

She was looking ahead but not seeing.

Her heart was still beating, but it felt hollow.

Her brain was still firing, but she couldn't think straight.

She walked on autopilot alongside Novak, Rory, Dax, and Maewyn. Her father's body was being dragged behind Rory on a makeshift stretcher. She wasn't leaving him behind. He deserved a proper burial and frankly she wasn't ready to truly say goodbye yet.

The edges of the stretcher left track marks in the dirt as they trudged away from the grove where Ash had left them forever.

It would be a long trip back to Zephyr.

Maewyn fell into step beside Adelia as they walked and spoke softly, breaking the silence. "I'm sorry, Adelia."

"How could you let him do that?" She still didn't understand.

"You know Ash. He's as stubborn as you are. And when it

comes to protecting those he cares about, he never second-guesses."

"There had to have been another way, though. We could have figured it out together..."

Maewyn shook her head. "You know as well as I do there wasn't time. If he hadn't made that decision, we likely would have died back there—" Maewyn stopped mid-sentence to gasp.

But it wasn't out of fear, it was relief.

Adelia looked around her, as little sprites came floating towards them from behind trees and under leaves. They were as cute as she imagined, but she found it hard to appreciate that at the moment.

They floated around her head like falling embers and converged around them.

One small sprite approached Maewyn and curtsied. "Let us heal you, Flaming Ice. In return for your courageousness and kindness in helping our kind. I see you put the barrier back in place before we got a chance to return, but we will be happy here in the forest. We are still in your debt."

Before she could stop herself, Adelia whispered, "Does that mean you can bring my dad back?" She was almost afraid to ask.

"I'm sorry, Daughter of the Storm, we cannot bring back the dead." She inclined her head to Adelia to convey her regrets.

She figured as much. But she had to ask anyway.

Then the sprites set to work on each of them.

Adelia watched in awe as their little hands glowed white and angelic, and the wounds Novak was sporting shrunk and healed. They continued until they were smooth and unblemished, erasing all evidence of the day's earlier events. They repeated the process and eventually made it to Adelia.

Her hands were burned, her back still healing. Her stump was aching more than it ever had before. Her lip was swollen and puffy along with a bruised face from the time spent in the dungeons. But those injuries weren't what hurt the most. The gaping crevasse in her heart was the worst of it. The hollow sense she felt at the loss of her dad and Ash. No physical injury would ever compare to those two events occurring in such quick succession. But she didn't want them to take away that pain. She needed to feel it. She needed to remember what she had lost today.

The sprites swarmed around her and her hands, back, face—all the places that were injured began to feel tingly and warm. She watched in awe as the skin on her hands reformed and the angry blisters were completely erased.

"Thank you." Tears burned her eyes.

It was one small grace after what had happened in the grove.

The road home would be a long one, filled with a dense grief.

She'd told herself from the beginning she'd do whatever it took to get her father back.

But she had ended up losing more than just him. She had lost a part of herself. And she wasn't quite sure how to get it back.

EPILOGUE

Parrots flew by on the canvas sky—their feathers like quills adding buoyant hues to the purples and pinks of the setting sun. Whenever Adelia needed to remember, she came up here; to The Perch. It was where she had first felt what it was like to control the wind, and the place where she and Ash had shared their first real moment together.

The memories this place held lifted her off the ground and took her far away to the corners of her dreams.

Dreams where she lived in a peaceful, beautiful world. A world where she got to live happily ever after with him, with her dad at her side.

But she had come to realize that she would never be able to move on.

That feeling of calm you get after a storm was exactly how she felt now. She knew what needed to be done.

She'd never accept the choice Ash had made for her. She hadn't been given a choice with her father. She had come to terms with the fact that she was never getting him back.

But Ash?

He didn't have the right to tell her what she could and couldn't do.

And there was no way she could forget, could just move on.

She refused to accept that.

She had never been the type of person—the type of Fae—to give up on the people she loved.

And she never had the chance to tell Ash that.

If she could infiltrate a deadly court of Fae and survive being locked up before escaping, then she could do it again.

She could figure out a way to break the barrier and get Ash back without condemning the rest of Faerie to another war.

The storm wasn't over. She *was* the storm and she was just getting started.

Adelia had her friends, her wind, and her lightning.

Nothing would stop her from taking back what was hers.

ADELIA'S
BEGINNER'S GUIDE
TO BIRDWATCHING

Birder: short form for birdwatcher.
Life List: a checklist of every bird in your country you check off like a bucket list as you see them.
Lifer: a bird species you have never seen before

How to become a birder

Put up a bird feeder in your backyard!
Look into hiking spots around you and get outside! Different species live in different areas so check out everything from fields, rivers, lakes, or forests.
Birds like early mornings the best so try and get out before noon!
Dress like a penguin not a parrot. (dark, breathable clothing! No neon colours)

Where to learn more:

1) Buy a field guide (either Roger Peterson or David Sibley if you live in North America)
2) Download the Merlin App to help with field identification
3) Sign-up for E-bird.org to keep track of your sightings
4) Join a bird identification help group on Facebook
5) Join a local naturalists club to make friends and learn more!

LOOK and LISTEN for birds

Gear you need:
- ☑ binoculars
- ☑ field guide
- ☑ hiking shoes
- ☑ bug spray
- ☑ sunscreen

PLAYLIST

Play with Fire - Sam Tinnesz
Big Bag Wold - Roses & Revolutions
Madness - Ruelle
Horns - Bryce Fox
Blood//Water - Grandson
Over - Honors
Demons - Imagine Dragons
Darkside - Neoni
Hypnotic - Zella Day
Body - Rosenfeld
Paint It, Black - Ciara
Castle - Halsey
Monsters - Ruelle
You should see me in a crown - Billie Eilish
We are warriors - Avril Lavigne
Man or a monster - Sam Tinnesz
Monsters - All Time Low

PRONUNCIATION GUIDE

Adelia: A - deal - ee - ah

Maewyn: May- win

Tadriel: Tad- ree- el

Teilio: Teal - ee - oh

ACKNOWLEDGMENTS

Trying to express how thankful I am to everyone that helped make this book a reality is so much harder than I ever could have imagined.

To my husband, Taylor (for those reading this - yes, his name is Taylor too) Thank you for being so incredibly supportive and encouraging throughout this entire process. You were everything I needed when I doubted myself and I love you so much.

To my parents and sister, Lynn, Chris and Mikaela. I lost track of how many times a week I would message the 'Fam Jam' group chat asking for opinions on everything from plot points, to grammar, to coming up with a marketing strategy. All of you have been supportive and I wouldn't have been able to do this without your unconditional love.

To my amazing Beta Readers, Mckenna Tosh, Emilie Leblanc, Courtney Nelson, Krystal McCausland, Hazel Starlene, Danielle Clark, Tara Hawthrone, Nicole Van Dan Heuvel, Emily Breitkopf, Merola Ishak and Kristen's Library. The book has changed so much from its first draft and all your feedback went into helping with that. I can't thank you all enough! And a special shoutout to Hazel, who I worked through literally every aspect of this book with. Your feedback is what made it what it is today. I can't thank you for your endless support and friendship enough.

To Brooke Passmore for designing my beautiful cover. It's everything I imagined and more.

To Emily, my editor. Thank you for helping me craft this book into the best version it could possibly be.

And finally, to the readers, thank you so much for supporting me and joining Adelia on her epic journey with Ash and the other Faerie Guards. I can't wait to bring you back to the world with book two :)

ABOUT THE AUTHOR

T.L. Wilson was born and raised in Ontario Canada where she now lives with her husband and cat Alucard – yes, that's Dracula backwards, and yes he's a biter. She is an avid bird-watcher and spends her spare time scouring the province for rare species to check off her list. If she's not birdwatching you can find her watching anime or curled up with a hot cup of tea and a good book. The Molten Key is Taylor's first novel.

You can find Taylor on Instagram as @drbookworm_ and Tiktok as @author.tlwilson